D1535165

A HISTORY OF THE CARE

AND STUDY OF THE

MENTALLY RETARDED

Frontispiece

Guggenbühl and a number of his patients on the Abendberg at sunrise: "The first photographic attempt of its kind, capable of future improvement. The small children are not in the picture except the two held by the nurses, because the others could not keep still for thirty seconds." (From J. J. Guggenbühl, Die Verhütung des Cretinismus und ihre neuesten Fortschritte. Mitteilungen an die schweizerische naturforschende Gesellschaft. Bern und Sankt Gallen, Huber & Company, 1853).

A HISTORY OF THE CARE AND STUDY OF THE MENTALLY RETARDED

(Second Printing)

By

LEO KANNER

Professor Emeritus of Child Psychiatry
The Johns Hopkins University
Honorary Consultant
The Johns Hopkins Hospital
Baltimore, Maryland

CHARLES C THOMAS • PUBLISHER
Springfield • Illinois • U.S.A.

Published and Distributed Throughout the World by

CHARLES C THOMAS • PUBLISHER

BANNERSTONE HOUSE

301-327 East Lawrence Avenue, Springfield, Illinois, U.S.A.

NATCHEZ PLANTATION HOUSE

735 North Atlantic Boulevard, Fort Lauderdale, Florida, U.S.A.

Library of Congress Catalog Card Number: 64-11659

First Printing, 1964

Second Printing, 1967

*With THOMAS BOOKS careful attention is given to all details of
manufacturing and design. It is the Publisher's desire to present books
that are satisfactory as to their physical qualities and artistic possibilities
and appropriate for their particular use. THOMAS BOOKS will be true
to those laws of quality that assure a good name and good will.*

·

Printed in the United States of America
J-2

TO

SUE ELLEN, JAMES DOUGLAS, and

STEVEN DAVID

Preface

In 1866, the publishing firm of Longmans, Green and Co., London, issued *A Manual for the Classification, Training, and Education of the Feeble-Minded, Imbecile, and Idiotic*. On page VIII of the introduction, the authors, P. M. Duncan and W. Millard, deplored the paucity of background material for their monograph. They wrote: "The scientific history of idiocy has yet to be produced; its data are scarce, and the study has not many charms."

Almost a whole century has passed since then, and still the data, though less scarce, have been scattered, some of them buried in journals and pamphlets not too easily accessible, some carried along by tradition as legends not substantiated by close scrutiny, some concerned mainly with specific, fragmentary details.

For years, it has been my ambition to gather the historical material for a comprehensive account of developments regarding the care and study of the mentally retarded. I must say that this task has had many charms, indeed. It was fascinating to observe the emergence of philanthropic, clerical, medical, psychologic, and sociologic interests in their relationship to general cultural phenomena. It was thrilling to trace the origins of new ideas and practices and to follow these trends as they spread, geographically and chronologically, to transcend national and linguistic boundaries and to become established features of our civilization. It was rewarding to become acquainted with the motives, personalities, and dedicated efforts of the pioneers.

All this has resulted in an attempt to offer a carefully documented narrative, with the hope that the fascination, the thrill, and the reward will be shared by the readers.

I wish to use this occasion to thank the personnel of the many libraries, in this country and abroad, who have been graciously helpful in my search for original sources.

LEO KANNER

Contents

A HISTORY OF THE CARE

AND STUDY OF THE

MENTALLY RETARDED

Chapter 1

The Dawn

I n discussing the history of the care of mental defectives, it has been customary to cite a few sporadic passages from Greek and Roman literature, from the Bible, the Talmud, and the Koran. Much, for instance, has been made of Mohammed's injunction, in the fourth verse of the fourth sura, to feed and house "those without reason" and to give them kindly words. The sum total of all those quotations, however, amounts to little beyond the fact that the existence of such persons was known and that occasionally friendliness toward them was advocated. There is no evidence of specific or organized efforts to do anything for their shelter, protection, or training. Though kind words were said about them from time to time, there was no practical application of any sort throughout many centuries.

The extreme paucity — almost nonexistence — of early sources has tempted searchers for any clue to exaggerate the significance of a few scattered reports. Thus Saint Nicholas Thaumaturgos (the Wonder-Worker), Bishop of Myra, who lived in the fourth century, has been described as a protector of the feebleminded. He may well have put in a good word for them now and then, but he is also regarded as the patron saint of *all* children, of sailors, and — of pawn brokers; the fact that at a much later date he was made to serve as the prototype of "Santa Claus" certainly does not qualify him to figure in the chronicles of mental deficiency.

3

Similar legends have been woven around a philanthropic lady whose name has been recorded variously as Euphrasia or Eupraxia. After the death of her husband Antigonus, a senator of Constantinople and a relative of Emperor Theodosius, she moved to her estates in Egypt where she "adopted the austere ways of the life of a nun" and cared for the homeless and the handicapped, possibly including some mental defectives.

This is about as much as can be said about any references in the annals of antiquity.

It seems that the lexicographers paid more attention to the terms used for mental defectives than their contemporaries paid to the people thus designated.

Fatuus (hence the words fatuous and fatuity) was a common Latin epithet. Bishop Isidorus Hispalensis (ca. 560-636) suggested two possible sources of this adjective: One refers to the participle of the verb *fari*, to speak: a *fatuus* is a person who understands neither what he says himself nor what others say. This is a bit reminiscent of the pseudo-etymological derivations based on "klang association" and reversal of the original meaning, such as *canis a non canendo*, or *lucus a non lucendo*.)

The second source goes back to the seeress Fatua, wife of Faun; persons driven to stupefaction by her prophesies were called *fatui*, and this term was then transferred to all "without a mind." (Being in love apparently has been deemed to have a similar effect — "infatuation" has the same origin; no wonder that the Romans coined the pun: *amantes amentes*.)

The author of another extensive Latin glossary, Aegidius Forcellinus, recorded the distinction between *fatuus* and *stultus*, the latter having obtuse senses, the former none.

The assumed characteristic of complete mindlessness was responsible for the synonym *amens*. Bishop Isidorus tried to make it clear in his dictionary that the *amens* has no mind at all, whereas a *demens* has retained part of his mind.

It is difficult to pinpoint the exact time at which the word *idiot* began to be employed in its present sense. Idiot derives from the Greek term which denotes "a private person." Hence, it came to mean "the common man." It then became reserved for "the unsophisticated layman without professional knowledge." As the next step, it was made to allude to "an ignorant, ill-informed individual." Ultimately, quite a bit later than in the writings of ancient Greeks, it was given the specific connotation of a mental defective.

The term *imbecile* underwent a similar semantic change in the course of time. Originally, *imbecillis* meant weak and was used by the Roman writers (e.g., Celsus) for any form of debility. Eventually, it was restricted to weakness of the mind, less severe than that of an idiot.

Etymology travels indeed along curious pathways — from the effects of Faun's wife (if the derivation is correct) to fatuity, from the status of a private person to idiocy, from general frailty to imbecility. Even more peculiar is the origin of a term which, though never employed by medical authors, has often served as a synonym for mental defectives. *Dunce* comes in straight line from John Duns Scotus, the scholastic theologian, who died in 1308. His works on religion, philosophy, and logic were textbooks in the universities, in which, as in Oxford, his followers were a predominating faction. In the 16th Century, his system was ridiculed first by the humanists and then by the reformers. The Dunsians or Dunses, on their side, railed against the "new learning," and the name Duns or Dunce, already the equivalent of "sophist" or "hair splitter," soon passed into the sense of "dull, obstinate person impervious to learning" and of "blockhead incapable of learning."

From ancient literature we know of only one use that was sometimes made of mental defectives. In Rome, it was not unusual for the wealthy to keep a "fool" or "jester" for the amusement of the household and its guests. Some of them acquired a great reputation, as did, for instance, Gabba, the fool of Emperor Augustus mentioned by Martial. Seneca related in one of his epistles (no. 50) to Lucilius: "You know that Herpaste, my wife's fool (*fatua*), was left on my hands as a hereditary charge, for I have a natural aversion to these monsters; and if I have a mind to laugh at a fool, I need not seek him far, I can laugh at myself. This fool has suddenly lost her sight. I am telling you a strange but true story. She is not aware that she is blind and constantly urges her keeper to take her out because she says my house is dark."

At a later time, the fools became the playthings of princes and the courts, as *fous* or *bouffons* in France, as *Hofnarren* in Germany. (The words fou and fool are of Latin origin. *Follis* meant a pair of bellows, a windbag; the plural *folles* meant puffed cheeks.) The jesters were recruited from persons with misshapen bodies and from mental defectives. Moreau, in a special study, asserted that the *bouffons* were for the most part imbeciles and *faibles d'esprit* "in the accepted scientific and medical sense of the word."

Some of the fools acquired fame, and a few even had their admiring biographers. The names Triboulet and Brusquet, at the court of King Francis I of France (1494-1547), and of Klaus Narr, who entertained the entourage of Duke Frederick the Wise of Saxony (1463-1525), are still carried in encyclopedias (e.g., Brockhaus Konversations-Lexicon, s.v. Hofnarr). It is known that under the reign of Charles V of France (1337-1380) the Province of Champagne was awarded the exclusive right to supply fools for his court.

Tradition has it that Tycho Brahe (1546-1601) had for his close companion an imbecile to whose mutterings the great astronomer listened as to a divine revelation. It is highly improbable that he knew of the Talmudic passage (Baba Bathra 12 a) which says that "from the day of the destruction of the Temple the art of prophesy was taken away (from the professionals) and given to fools." This passage may be responsible for the Yiddish proverb according to which "a complete fool is half a prophet."

The kept fools, of course, occupied an exceptional position among the mental defectives or otherwise handicapped. The vast majority of idiots and imbeciles did not fare so well. It is true that in many "uncivilized" areas they were regarded superstitiously as blessed "infants of the good God" and were allowed to roam unmolested.

It was during the period of "enlightenment" and "reform" that the mental defectives were at their worst. It was then that many of them became victims of the prevailing demonism. Martin Luther referred to the feebleminded as godless and reported this occurrence in one of his *Table Talks*:

"Eight years ago, there was one at Dessau whom I, Martinus Luther, saw and grappled with. He was twelve years old, had the use of his eyes and all his senses, so that one might think that he was a normal child. But he did nothing but gorge himself as much as four peasants or threshers. He ate, defecated and drooled and, if anyone tackled him, he screamed. If things didn't go well, he wept. So I said to the Prince of Anhalt: 'If I were the Prince, I should take this child to the Moldau River which flows near Dessau and drown him.' But the Prince of Anhalt and the Prince of Saxony, who happened to be present, refused to follow my advice. Thereupon I said: 'Well, then the Christians shall order the Lord's Prayer to be said in church and pray that the dear Lord take the Devil away.' This was done daily in Dessau and the changeling died in the following year. When Luther was asked why he had made such a recommendation, he replied that he was firmly of the opinion that such changelings were merely a mass of flesh, a *massa carnis,* with no soul. For it is in the Devil's power that he corrupts people who have reason and souls when he possesses them. The Devil sits in such changelings where their soul should have been!"

While the reformers, including John Calvin, thus had a ready-made explanation of mental deficiency, medicine was for a long time completely unconcerned about the whole issue. Until the end of the 18th Century there were extremely few references to it in the medical and the would-be medical literature. It is easy to agree with Weygandt, who wrote in the introduction to his classical monograph on idiocy and imbecility: "While the writers of antiquity gave vivid and correct descriptions of specific psychotic conditions—e.g., Hippocrates of epilepsy and Aretaeus of mania and melancholia, — idiocy has rarely been mentioned until very recently." Any bibliographic quest for publications in the areas of psychiatry, neurology, and psychology leads one invariably to Heinrich Laehr's compilation of the pertinent writings from 1459 to 1799. In this magnificent collection, which comprises two huge volumes and a separate index of authors and subjects, there is among the many thousands of recorded and sometimes annotated items not one, however faint, allusion to mental deficiency, except for the evidence of sporadic interest in cretinism toward the end of the Middle Ages.

References

Aegidius Forcellinus: *Totius Latinitatis Lexicon*. Prati, 1865, s.v. amens.

Bernstein, I.: *Jüdische Sprichwörter and Redensarten*. Warsaw, J. Kauffmann, 1908, p. 173.

Gazeau, A.: *Les bouffons*. Paris, Hachette, 1882.

Isidorus Hispalensis: *Originum seu Etymologiarum libri XX*. Augustae Vindelicorum, Zainder, 1742. s.v., fatuus.

Kirchhoff, T.: *Grundriss einer Geschichte der deutschen Irrenpflege*. Berlin, August Hirschwald, 1890.

Laehr, H.: *Die Literatur der Psychiatrie, Neurologie und Psychologie von 1459 bis 1799*. Berlin, Georg Reimer, 1899.

Luther, M.: *Colloquia Mensalia*. *London*, William Du-Gard, 1652, p. 387.

—————: *Sämtliche Schriften*, Ausgabe von K. E. Förstermann, Band XXII, pp. 56 f., 69 f., 70 f.

Martialis, Marcus Valerius: *Epigrammata*, X 101.

Moreau, P.: *Fous et bouffons*. Paris, Baillière et fils, 1885.

Oxford Dictionary of the English Language, s.v. dunce.

Skeat, W. W.: *An Etymological Dictionary of the English Language*. Oxford, Clarenden Press, 1958, s.v. fool.

Wallin, J. E. W.: *Education of Mentally Handicapped Children*. New York, Harper and Brothers, 1955. Chapter I: Historical Orientation.

Weygandt, W.: *Idiotie und Imbezillität*. Leipzig, Franz Deuticke, 1915.

Chapter 2

Beginnings and the Beginners

ALMOST SUDDENLY, interest in the mental defectives began to flare up in the first half of the 19th Century, spreading from France and Switzerland to the rest of the civilized portion of Europe and to the United States of America. A number of developments converged to explain this unprecedented spurt. Some of them are closely connected with the ideas with which Rousseau, the Encyclopedists, Pestalozzi, and Fellenberg are identified. Those were the times when spokesmen arose who vigorously espoused the causes of thitherto oppressed or neglected groups — the slaves, the prisoners, the insane, the blind, and the deaf. It is, as a matter of fact, remarkable that the principal pioneer in the training of idiots in France carried out his work at an institution for deafmutes and that the first "experimental school" for idiots in America was housed in an institution for the blind. It is also significant that the early sponsors of the education of mental defectives openly declared that they derived much of their inspiration from Jacob Rodrigues Pereire and his accomplishments in the teaching of deafmutes.

The first explorations were undertaken by enthusiastic young men in their early to middle twenties who usually were not encouraged by the established authority. Itard proceeded against Pinel's better judgment, and Seguin had in Esquirol a benevolent, though highly skeptical, friend and mentor. This was, in a way, not surprising in view of the goals that the fervent youngsters

9

had set for themselves. Guggenbühl had set out to "cure" cretins, and Itard originally intended to lead the "wild boy of Aveyron" on to a normal existence. Both of them failed and yet they and others inaugurated methods and facilities which were soon incorporated in the western civilization.

The whole movement cannot be fully appreciated without a review of the personalities and individual efforts of the men who originated the educational and institutional work with the feeble-minded.

It would be difficult, if indeed possible, to assign all credit to any one person. No such claims were made, except by J. E. Belhomme (1800-1880) who, in a pamphlet published in 1824, had advocated education of the retarded "to ameliorate the unfortunate situation" and expressed the opinion that "idiots are educable in accordance with their degree of idiocy." In 1835, he wrote an angry letter to the French Academy of Science, "reclaiming" the priority of his ideas. In 1843, he reprinted the earlier pamphlet; in the introduction, he deplored the fact that "the modern authors seem to disregard my studies; they have omitted my name as though I might overshadow their success." Bitterly he concluded: "Those who seem interested in putting themselves forth as the first discoverers, appear to ignore the writings of which I am the author." Careful perusal of the "Essai" fails to disclose any originality of thought or any suggestion of practical application.

Reference

Belhomme, J. E.: *Essai sur l'idiotie, propositions sur l'éducation des idiots, mise en rapport avec leur degré d'intelligence.* Paris, Germer-Baillière, 1824. Reprinted, Paris, Dondey Dupré. 1843.

Jacob Rodrigues Pereire (1715-1780) was born April 11, 1715, in Berlanga, a small town in Spanish Estremadura. His Jewish father had been obliged to profess Christianity, and Jacob was baptized with the name Francisco Antonio Rodrigues. After his father's death, his mother fled with her children to escape the charge that she had relapsed into heresy and eventually settled in Bordeaux. Jacob studied anatomy and physiology and became actively interested in the education of congenital deafmutes. On January 19, 1747, he presented his method at the Académie Royale de Belles Lettres of Caen and received much praise for his labors. On June 11, 1749, he demonstrated the results of his work at the Academy of Science in Paris, in the presence of many notables, including Buffon. The unheard-of observation of a reading and speaking deafmute created such a sensation that King Louis XV asked Pereire and his pupil (son of d'Étavigny of La Rochelle) to appear at court and was so impressed that he granted him an annual pension of 800 francs as a token of esteem.

Pereire distinguished himself in many other respects. He worked out a method to determine the most advantageous way of supplementing the action of the wind on large sailing vessels. In 1760, he was made a member of the Royal Society of London. In 1765, he was appointed as the King's interpreter for Spanish and Portuguese. Through his influence, Jews from Portugal received in 1777 the right to settle in France.

However, his fame rests principally on the introduction and application of the idea that deafmutes, thought hopelessly unchangeable until then, could be helped to learn how to communicate with others. He taught them a simplified sign language ("dactylologia") and invented an arithmetical machine to teach them how to calculate. Celebrated men sat in at his lessons: Buffon, Diderot, d'Alembert, and others. Rousseau, who lived in the same street as Pereire, quoted him as "the only person in his time who could make mutes talk." His patience, hard work, and courage served as a model for others, especially in connection with educational possibilities for the blind and the feebleminded. Though Pereire himself had no direct contact with intellectually deficient persons, his work with the deafmutes gave much encouragement to Itard and to Seguin; the latter expressed his indebtedness to Pereire on many occasions and more specifically in a separate monograph. Barr (1904, p. 41) declared categorically: "Without Pereire, Itard had been impossible."

Pereire married rather late in life (November 5, 1766). His descendants played an important part in the history of France. Two grandsons, Emile and Isaac, were active in the promotion and organization of railroads, owned and edited several of the leading French periodicals, and were instrumental in the establishment of savings banks throughout the country. A great-grandson, Eugène, served at one time as French consul-general in Persia.

Pereire died September 15, 1780, in Paris. His remains are buried in the Montmartre cemetery.

References

Hément, F. J.: *Rodrigues Pereire, premier instituteur des sourds et muets.* Paris, Abbéville, 1875.

Robinson, V.: *Pereire and His Pupils. Med. Leaves,* 3; 147-156. 1941.

Seguin, E.: *Jacob Rodrigues Pereire, sur sa vie et ses tràvaux.* Paris, Baillière, 1847.

Jean Marc Gaspard Itard (1774-1838), born at Oraison in Provence, leaped into prominence as one of the originators of the education of the feebleminded because of his efforts on behalf of "the wild boy of Aveyron."

Itard was destined to enter a business career but those were hectic days in France when he had reached the age of settling down to a steady occupation. His country was at war with most of the rest of Europe and, to avoid conscription, he enlisted as an assistant surgeon in a military hospital. He became fascinated by his work, pursued the study of medicine with great zeal, and soon gained distinction as a physician. His first major assignment on the medical staff of the Institution for Deafmutes in Paris directed his interests toward the training of the inmates and toward the scientific study of the organs of hearing and speech. His treatise on the diseases of the ear, published in 1821, is regarded as the historical event which laid the foundation of modern otology.

Shortly after Itard had started on his job at twenty-five years of age, a young boy, approximately eleven or twelve years old, was brought to the institution by the Abbé Sicard Bonnaterre, Professor of Natural History at the Central School of the Department of Aveyron. This boy, sometimes referred to as Victor or Juvenis Averionensis, had stirred the fantasy of the philosophers and the scientists of those days. There are different versions of the story about his early background and about the manner of his capture. As reported by P. J. Virey (Dictionnaire d'histoire naturalle du genre humain, Vol. XI, 1803-331), a naked child was seen, who ran away from human beings and who roamed through the woods of Caunes in the Department of Tarn searching for roots and acorns for food. He was caught but escaped soon afterwards. In 1798, he was again caught by three hunters, brought to Caunes, escaped again and lived like a vagabond for six months, "exposed to the cold of the coldest winters." One winter day, he entered the house of a dyer outside the city of St. Sernin, wearing only the remains of a shirt which had been put on him half a year earlier. They gave him potatoes, which he ate raw, as well as chestnuts and acorns; he refused any other food. He did not speak any language and uttered inarticulate sounds. "Wherever he was, he would answer the calls of nature and had no idea of modesty."

The boy was taken to the Hospice St. Afrique and then turned over to the naturalist Bonnaterre, who in turn got Itard interested in him. Opinions differed about him. Some observers declared him to be a swindler. Philippe Pinel, the famous psychiatrist, decided after an examination that the boy's wildness was a fake and that he was "an incurable idiot, inferior to domestic animals." Still others wondered whether he represented a specimen of what Rousseau had thought were the advantages of "natural existence."

The boy's appearance created considerable controversy and a number of children were recalled who had been reported previously as being discovered after living wildly in the fields and woods, some of them nurtured by animals. The authenticity of some of the sources is questionable. Carl Linnaeus (1707-1778) listed ten such instances as a variety of the genus Homo, speaking of them as homo ferus (wild), tetrapus (walking on all four), mutus, and hirsutus (hairy): (1) Juvenis lupinus Hessensis, found among wolves in 1544; (2) Juvenis ursinus Lithuanus, brought up by bears (1661); (3) Juvenis ovinus Hibernius, nursed by wild sheep in Ireland (reported by Tulpius, 1672); (4) Juvenis bovinus Bambergensis, found among a herd of oxen (according to Camerarius); (5) Juvenis Hannoveranus,

"Wild Peter" of Hanover, found by a Townsman of Hameln in 1724, brought in 1726 to London, where he became a sensation; King George I made a present of him to the then Princess of Wales, who later became Queen Caroline; Swift immortalized him in a humorous production, *It cannot rain but it pours, or London strewed with Rareties;* (6) Pueri Pyrenaici (1719); "a dubious case": Zingg; (7) Puella Transisalana, found in 1717 in the Dutch province of Over-Yssel; (8) Puella Campanica, discovered in the Champagne in 1731; (5) Johannes Leodicensis, or John of Liège (Boerhaave); (10) Puella Karpfensis (1767).

Interest in feral or wild children has by no means subsided. One need only mention the story of Kaspar Hauser (who was made the central figure of a novel by Jakob Wassermann) and the excitement created not too long ago by the accounts about Kamala and Amala, rescued from a wolf den in a jungle near Midnapore, India, on October 17, 1920. R. M. Zingg has made an exhaustive analysis of the extensive literature on "feral man" (*Wolf Children and Feral Man.* New York, Harper 1939).

When Victor of Aveyron was brought to Itard, the young physician could not accept Pinel's prognosis of irreversibility. He believed that the boy was mentally arrested because of social and educational neglect, that he had acquired idiocy through isolation, a sort of mental atrophy from disuse. He undertook to transfer the boy "from savagery to civilization, from natural life to social life." He set before himself five main objectives: (1) To render social life more congenial to the boy by making it more like the wild life he had recently kept. (2) To excite his nervous sensibility with varied and energetic stimuli and supply his mind with the raw impression of ideas. (3) To extend the range of his ideas by creating new wants and expanding his relations with the world around him. (4) To lead him to the use of speech by making it necessary that he should imitate. (5) To apply himself to the satisfaction of his growing physical wants, and from this lead on to the application of his intelligence to the objects of instruction.

Itard labored for five years. He did not achieve his goal. When the boy "broke out in a wild storm of passion" attributed to puberty, his teacher gave up, feeling that he had failed in

FRONTISPIECE.

The Wild Boy, found in the Woods in Aveyron.

Printed for R. Phillips. N:71. S: Pauli Church Yard. March 1. 1802.

Victor of Aveyron. (From *An Historical Account of the Discovery and Education of A SAVAGE MAN or of the First Developments, Physical and Moral, of the YOUNG SAVAGE Caught in the Woods near Aveyron in the Year 1798.* London, printed for Richard Phillips, No. 71, St. Paul's Church-Yard, 1802.)

his mission. Victor lived for many years in custodial care and died in 1828.

Nevertheless, the French Academy of Science applauded not only the effort but also the fact that the boy, who initially was mute, walked on all fours, drank water while lying flat on the ground, and bit and scratched everyone interfering with his actions, showed some remarkable changes. He had learned to recognize objects, identify letters of the alphabet, comprehend the meaning of many words, apply names to objects and parts of objects, make "relatively fine" sensory discriminations, and "preferred the social life of civilization to an isolated existence in the wild." The Academy recognized that Itard had made a positive contribution to educational science. He had proved that even a severe mental defective could be improved to some extent by appropriate training. This is a part of the statement issued by the Academy:

"This class of the Academy acknowledges that it was impossible for the institutor to put in his lessons, exercises, and experiments more intelligence, sagacity, patience, and courage; and that, if he has not obtained a great success, it must be attributed not to any lack of zeal or talent, but to the imperfection of the organs of the subject upon which he worked. The Academy, moreover, cannot see without astonishment how he could succeed as far as he did, and think that to be just toward Monsieur Itard, and to appreciate the real worth of his labors, the pupil ought to be compared only with himself; we should remember what he was when placed in the hands of his physician, see what he is now; and more, consider the distance separating his starting point from that which he has reached; and by how many new and ingenious modes of teaching this gap has been filled. The pamphlet of Monsieur Itard contains also the exposition of a series of extremely singular and interesting phenomena of fine judicious observations; and presents a combination of highly instructive processes, capable of furnishing science with new data, the knowledge of which can but be extremely useful to all persons engaged in the teaching of youth."

Publications by Itard

De l'éducation d'un homme sauvage. Paris, Goujon. 1801.

Rapports et mémoires sur le sauvage d'Aveyron. L'idiotie et la surdimutité, avec une appréciation de ces rapports par Delasiauve. Préface par Bourneville. Éloge d'Itard par Bousquet. Paris, F. Alcan. 1804.

Rapport fait a son Excellence le Ministre de l'Intérieur sur les nouveaux développements et l'état actuel du sauvage d'Aveyron. Paris, J. J. Marcel. 1807.

Traité des maladies d'oreille et de l'audition. 2 vol. Paris, Méquignon-Marvis. 1821.

Biographical Data on Itard

Bousquet, J. B. E.: *Éloge historique de Itard.* Paris, Cosson. 1839.

Kanner, L.: Itard, Seguin, Howe — Three Pioneers in the Education of Retarded Children. *Am. J. Ment. Deficiency,* 65: 1-10, 1960.

Silberstein, R. M., and Irwin, H. Jean Marc Gaspard, Itard and the Savage of Aveyron: An Unsolved Diagnostic Problem in Child Psychiatry. *J. Amer. Acad. Child Psychiat.,* 1:314-322, 1962.

Johann Jacob Guggenbühl was born August 16, 1816, at Meilen on Lake Zurich in Switzerland. While a student of medicine, he was impressed by the interest in cretinism shown by Ignaz Paul Vitalis Troxler, physician and philosopher, who discussed it as a form of endemic human degeneration and expressed the hope that something might be done for those afflicted.

In 1836, twenty-year old Guggenbühl, while passing through the village of Seedorf in the canton of Uri, was stirred by the sight of a "dwarfed, crippled cretin of stupid appearance" mumbling the Lord's Prayer before a wayside cross. He followed the man to a nearby shack where the cripple's mother related that she had taught the prayer to her son during his childhood without too much difficulty and that since then he had gone to pray before the cross regularly every day at the same hour in any kind of weather. She added that because of extreme poverty she had been unable to provide any further education for him and had to sit idly by while watching him deteriorate from year to year.

The young physician wondered whether more might have been achieved if there had been an opportunity for consistent and intensive training. He could not go along with the traditional

Johann Jakob Guggenbühl, director of Abendberg.

House near Meilen in which Guggenbühl was born.
(The house is still in existence.)

The shrine in Seedorf where Guggenbühl observed the praying cretin.

The institution on the Abendberg in its early days. (Reproduced from *Geschichte der Schwachsinnigenfursorge in der Schweiz* by K. Alther. Glarus, Glarner Nachrichten, 1923.)

notion that idiotic children were wholly inaccessible to any ameliorative efforts. In going over the literature on cretinism, he found innumerable treatises on symptomatology and etiology but not a single word about the possibility of remedial endeavor. Scientific research, he felt, was only one aspect of the problem. What was needed, in addition, was personal interest "of the kind which John Howard and Elizabeth Fry had in prison inmates, Thomas Clarkson, William Wilberforce, and Thomas Powell Buxton had in slaves, and Hans Egede had in the indolent Greenlanders."

Guggenbühl was determined to devote his life to the "cure and prophylaxis" of cretinism. Nowhere in the world was there a residential arrangement for the teaching and the medical care of mentally defective children. A few rudimentary attempts had not gotten far.

Guggenbühl was not disheartened. With unflagging ardor, he undertook many trips to the affected areas to learn from personal observation as much as he could "about the condition, incidence, and causes of cretinism." In order to try out therapeutic experiments, he settled as a general practitioner in the Kleinthal of Glarus. He came to the conclusion that residential care in a suitable environment was an indispensable necessity. Realizing that he needed experience in the field of education, he conferred with Philip Emanuel von Fellenberg who in 1799, when he was twenty-eight years old, had built a model pedagogic establishment at Hofwyl, which eventually became a training center for teachers. Fellenberg, greatly impressed by the young man, wrote to him: "Your noble decision to found an institution for cretins has moved me deeply. It is a labor of love which is bound to result in many blessings. If you could see your way to accept a post as physician at Hofwyl, we might have a closer interchange of ideas than it would be possible if we were separated from each other."

Guggenbühl gave up his small practice and took up the position in 1839. When his patients urged him to remain, he replied: "If general practice were my life's aim, I should not trade my work among you for an appointment at a royal court. But God has chosen another course for me, and I must heed his call." He left his few patients behind, entering upon a preparation that should, so he hoped, enable him to bring relief to the many.

His ideas provoked criticism. A newspaper in Berne was especially vitriolic and ridiculed the scheme as a hare-brained chimera. Guggenbühl felt, therefore, that he ought to get authoritative support. He issued an eloquent appeal, entitled *Christenthum und Humanität im Blick auf den Cretinismus*, which he addressed to the Swiss Association of Natural Sciences (*Schweizerische Naturwissenschaftliche Gesellschaft*). This learned body named a committee which concluded its deliberations as follows: "It certainly would be to great advantage to proceed against this sad malady in early childhood, at a time when cretinism has not become firmly intrenched. The erudition and zeal of Dr. Guggenbühl would, if he were to be the director of the planned hospital, be the best guarantee for the success of the enterprise."

The plan came to the attention of Karl Kasthofer (1777-1853), a Swiss forester, who had long been an advocate of the substitution of colonies for closed-in prisons and almshouses. He had proved that the cultivation of plant life, and hence colonization, was possible in the higher mountainous regions. Considering that cretinism, abundant in the valleys, was not known to occur at greater elevations, he put at Guggenbühl's disposal a tract of some 40 acres on the Abendberg, near Interlaken, in the canton of Berne, more than 4000 feet above sea level, 100 feet from the summit. The southern slope was soon dotted with cottages and the daily ministrations were turned over to the Diakonissen, Evangelical Sisters of Mercy. There was a central structure with a large assembly hall, playrooms, and bathing facilities, and another building was designed for training courses given to prospective attendants and teachers.

Guggenbühl set forth in an all-out attempt to build up his patients with all means available. He considered pure mountain air as a prime requisite and, in his era of literary neo-romanticism, extolled in poetical terms the curative effects of the beauty of Nature. He gave heed to what he postulated as a good diet: goat's milk, white bread, eggs, vegetables, rice, and some meat. There was an emphasis on care of the body through baths, massage, and physical exercises. He tried out a variety of medications, especially calcium, copper, and zinc preparations. At the same time, he went about to develop sensory perceptions, beginning with primitive excitations and progressing from there to more refined and more complex stimuli. He proceeded from the conviction that, as he once wrote, "the immortal soul is essentially the same in every creature born of woman," and tried to "awaken" the "souls" of his patients through habituation to regular routine, memory exercises, and speech training. He even introduced into the group two normally intelligent, though neglected, children of a servant who "brought life into the institution."

This work was hailed everywhere as a major reform. It may at first glance seem peculiar that enthusiasm was high even in those areas in which cretinism did not exist, except in sporadic instances. But in those days, most authorities regarded cretinism and all forms of idiocy and imbecility as the same phenomenon, the difference being one of degree and presence or absence of physical deformities. Hence, the methods of the Abendberg were assessed as applicable to all feebleminded children, and not specifically to cretins.

Guggenbühl's fame spread rapidly throughout the civilized world. He helped matters along, it is true, by propagating his ideas in extensive travels and publicizing the Abendberg in many pamphlets. He did not hesitate to solicit endorsements from notables whom he knew to be favorably disposed, nor did he refrain from including their eulogies in his communications. He quoted this message from Ernst Freiherr von Feuchtersleben, the celebrated Austrian poet, physician, philosopher, and educational reformer: "The brief reports which you issue from time to time are not only useful but very necessary for the general public which needs enlightenment about this matter. The manner in which these notes are written is just right because they accomplish the combined purpose of gaining hearts and heads for the cause, bringing it to the attention of the public, and inviting support. The Abendberg must certainly be regarded as the center of all efforts and research concerning this important issue. Keep up this work so auspiciously begun!"

Guggenbühl made sure to let his readers know what the psychiatrist Christian Friedrich Nasse (1778-1851) of Bonn had written to him: "Since the start of your undertaking, I have followed your procedures with joyous consent . . . I am convinced that the aim of your beneficent institution will be achieved victoriously. It is highly meritorious to take the decisive first step for so large a group of unfortunates who have lived on hopelessly so long as not even the thought of the possibility of helping them has occurred to anyone."

The Abendberg became the destination of pilgrimages made by physicians, philanthropists, and writers from many lands, who promptly published glowing reports when they went back home. Countess Ida Hahn-Hahn (1805-1880), a writer of best-selling novels and travel diaries, had an idiotic daughter, born in the year when she sued for and obtained a divorce from her psychopathically brutal husband; she heard of the Abendberg, went to visit the place, was enormously impressed, made a substantial monetary contribution (7,500 Swiss francs), and published in 1843 a brochure which appeared in Berlin. Samuel Gridley Howe, who was about to establish in Massachusetts the first institution for idiotic children in the western hemisphere, inspected the Abendberg and, overwhelmed by what he saw, pronounced: "The holy mount it should be called!" In fact, many of the visitors were not merely satisfied to sing the praises of Guggenbühl and his work but urged the citizens and governments of their countries to organize similar institutions. Guggenbühl proudly referred to the many newly established places as foster children (*Pflegetöchter*) of the Abendberg.

Charles Albert of Savoy, King of Sardinia, appointed a committee to study cretinism on the mainland of his realm. In the report, published in 1848, the Abendberg was recommended as a model and Guggenbühl was described as a man "moved by the most honorable sentiment of commiseration for his unfortunate cretin compatriots." Louis-André Gosse (1778-1851), psychiatrist in Geneva, endorsed him similarly in the same year: "We are convinced of the purity of his principles and of the truthfulness of his assertions."

Guggenbühl found an especially resounding echo in England. The Abendberg was visited on September 4, 1842, by William Twining, who went home and sang its praises in a monograph, in which he declared: "It is, in truth, a noble and exalted idea that, through human exertions, a mind may be awakened in what was apparently a senseless mass, and that even education may be extended to those who have been hitherto considered beyond the reach of instruction and incapable of intercourse with their fellow creatures. And what brighter and more glorious page can there be in the history of Switzerland if a century hence it should be recorded that all Europe helped to exterminate cretinism?"

Guggenbühl was indeed an internationally famous man in those days. He was made an honorary or corresponding member of the Swiss Society of Natural Science, the Medico-Chirurgical Society of Zurich, the Imperial-Royal Society of Physicians in Vienna, the Academy of Medicine in Turin, the Imperial Russian Society of Physicians in St. Petersburg, the Medical Society of Erlangen, the Rhenish Association for Natural Sciences and Medicine in Bonn, the Association for Governmental Medicine in Baden, the National Society of Medicine in Marseille, and the Medical Society of Strassburg.

Institutions, shaped in the image of the Abendberg and often staffed by persons trained there, were started in Germany, Austria, Great Britain, the Netherlands, the Scandinavian countries, the United States of America, and elsewhere. Guggenbühl went from place to place, lecturing, counseling, accepting expressions of homage and adoration, heralded as the man who had brought the gospel of new life for a thitherto neglected portion of mankind.

There were from the beginning voices of criticism which, however, were for a long time drowned by the panegyrics which came from all sides. (Auzouy wrote about those days: "*S'il eut quelques détracteurs, ceux-ci ne furent que de légères touches dans le soleil, brillant alors de tout son éclat.*") Monarchs, famous writers, medical men, reformers, and other celebrities vied in doing him honor. But some people felt that he promised too much. There was irritation about the unctuous manner in which he all but identified himself with the will of God. Thus, for instance, he introduced one of his papers in a medical journal with these words: "Switzerland has indisputably been selected by Divine Providence to shine forth before the other nations in the realization of blissful ideas," and then went on to present the Abendberg as one of God's merciful miracles, with himself as the man chosen to perform them.

Eventually more and more people recognized that idiotic children — cretins or otherwise — were not "cured" by the prescribed methods. Their frustrations were quickly converted into animosity against Guggenbühl. He found fewer and fewer defenders. As early as in 1853, he began to feel that his star was not too firmly installed in the skies. In that year he wrote:

"The antecedents of Swiss cultural history are unfortunately anything but encouraging for new ideas and endeavors, for they show what inexpressible difficulties they encounter and how one group of wretched troublemakers is always ready to destroy what others have built with laborious effort. The most deterring example of rascality against the meritorious inventor of a natural method of education and instruction has been depicted by one of our historians: 'Shocking is the story of the last days of Pestalozzi. Insulting pamphlets pelted down upon him and even the *Neue Züricher Zeitung* dared to compare the old bent man to a dog that crawls behind the stove when a stick is waved before him. Unscrupulous paid pamphletists had the nerve not only to question the value of his life's work but even to deny it and they accomplished that. Pestalozzi became confused about himself and did likewise.' This is a psychological proof how necessary it is to react to such shameful troublemakers with nothing more than the contempt which they deserve."

This statement was contained in a book dedicated to Freiherr Christian Karl Josias von Bunsen (1799-1860) who had given Guggenbühl much moral support when he was the Prussian ambassador to Switzerland from 1839-1841 and later when he served as envoy to England. It is therefore interesting to note that the major impetus for his ultimate defeat came from the British minister to Berne, Gordon. There were a few English patients on the Abendberg, and Gordon decided to pay them a visit. He did so on April 13, 1858. He found "the children in a most neglected condition and the whole institution (which the guide at first refused to show him) in disgusting disorder." When he asked to see the bedroom of one of the children, he was told that "the key to the room had been misplaced." Guggenbühl himself was not present at the time, having left for an extended trip in November 1857. Gordon reported his impression to the government of the canton. Rumors about mismanagement had been rife for quite some time. A number of former admirers had withdrawn their endorsement. Dr. Demme, who had been one of the most sanguine heralds of the opening of the Abendberg, implored its director to allow an impartial medical examination of the inmates at the time of their admission and at the time of their discharge; this plea went unheeded. An unpleasant incident had preceded Gordon's complaint: A patient had fallen from a precipice and his disappearance was not noticed until a peasant found the body some time later. Another child had died and the carpenter who was called to make a coffin reported that he found the body in a decomposed state; when he asked why he had not been summoned sooner, he was told by the personnel that they "hadn't gotten around to it."

Hence it is not surprising that, when the British minister expressed his indignation, the government promptly (on April 20, 1858) ordered an official investigation to be conducted by two physicians, Vogt and Verdat. In a pamphlet (*Der Abendberg wie er ist*), these "officially established facts" were put forth:

1. Guggenbühl was guilty of deceiving people in his country and elsewhere by calling his establishment a *Kretinen-Heilanstalt*. At most one-third of the inmates were cretins. (The pamphlet went so far as to accuse Guggenbühl of "smuggling in" normal children whom he presented to astonished audiences as cured cretins.)

2. Normal children were kept from attending the public schools by housing them on the Abendberg.

3. Not a single cretin had ever been cured on the Abendberg.

4. While Guggenbühl originally claimed that he intended to treat infant cretins, he took in persons up to twenty-three of age and none less than five years old.

5. There was no medical supervision. The director was away from four to six months each year and made no provisions for a substitute.

6. While at first he had employed well-trained instructors, some of whom went on to do creditable work in other newly founded institutions, the Abendberg had been without a teacher for several years. Guggenbühl tried to explain this, as he had done in his open letter to Lord Ashley, by pointing out that women are more loving and better qualified to care for the unfortunate children. However, at the time of the investigation, there were only two uneducated peasant women on the grounds.

7. Heating facilities, nutrition, water supply, ventilation in the dormitories, and clothing were inadequate.

8. The director never kept books nor accounted to anybody for the munificent donations which he received for his institution.

9. No records were kept about the patients' progress.

The pamphlet acknowledged that Guggenbühl had begun the project "out of pure and unselfish love" but deplored that this was soon adulterated by vanity, meeting all criticism with the air of a misunderstood martyr for a holy cause, embellishment of treatment results, and the exploitation of religious sentiments.

As a result of the investigation, the Swiss Association of Natural Sciences withdrew its sponsorship and its support. The Abendberg was closed at a time when other institutions, shaped after it, began to flourish everywhere in Europe and in the United States of America.

Guggenbühl withdrew to Montreaux where, having never married, he lived alone, writing jeremiads for which he found no publisher, though a medical journal in Vienna (1860) and one in Berlin (1862) did each bring out a short paper of his. He died on February 2, 1863, at forty-seven years of age. A half-page obituary by Georgens and Deinhard in the *Allgemeine Wiener medizinische Zeitschrift* (1863, Vol. VIII, p. 53) gave him restrained credit for "having effectively roused interest in the care of idiots."

One is entitled to wonder how it was possible for him to amass enough earthly goods to enable him to leave in his will not less than 600,000 Swiss francs to the Moravian Brothers (of the Church of the Brotherhood) to continue his institution. There is no record how this money was used eventually. The Abendberg was sold in 1867 and served as a resort hotel. Encyclopedias later in the 19th Century mention a dairy establishment at the place.

Guggenbühl may have had his faults. His premises may have been erroneous. His commitments, once made, may have pushed him into inflexibility and denial of reality which invited rebuff. But the perusal of his writings leaves no doubt as to his sincere belief in the curability of cretins, however unwarranted this belief may have been. His travels may have deflected him from necessary administrative responsibilities, which he left in the hands of his stepfather, about whom nothing is known beyond the fact that he let the place run down during his son's frequent and long absences.

But Guggenbühl must be acknowledged as the indisputable originator of the idea and practice of the institutional care for feebleminded individuals. The hundreds of institutions now in existence derive in direct line from the Abendberg.

The attitude toward the man has gone through three phases. The first, between 1840 and the middle 1850's, was one of enormous admiration bordering on worship, shared by the great physicians and other scientists of that era. The second, lasting for about two decades, abounded in derogatory remarks about the "so-called" Kretinen-Heilanstalt which *"n'a jamais été qu'une duperie,"* and its founder who was described as a swindler, a quack, a charlatan, an embezzler, and a bigot. The third phase began when animosities cooled off and his position in history could be assessed less passionately without the initial idolization and without the subsequent unattenuated condemnation. This attitude is best exemplified by the following two quotations:

The Reverend Heinrich Matthias Sengelmann (1821-1899) wrote after a brief summary of Guggenbühl's work: "Not to sit in judgment on the man, the bow string was strained beyond its strength. Too much had been promised. To those who insisted on seeing the fulfillment of all promises it was necessary to present parade horses, and this procedure could not satisfy those observers who penetrated into the character of it. The incense of adulation weakened his sober judgment. To this must be added that during his frequent absences from the Abendberg abuses crept in which he could not at once detect or correct. Later, once suspicion was aroused, his religious tendencies, which had at first been tolerated, were made to appear as the source of these abuses, and he was unjustly stamped as a hypocrite."

In 1904, Martin W. Barr did his best to restore the respect for Guggenbühl's significance as a pacemaker. He wrote: "In reviewing his methods, which in the main meet the demands of and are endorsed by latter-day experience, we cannot but acknowledge the deep insight gained by this man into the needs of many forms of defect, in his self-devoted study of the one (cretinism); an insight not alone into details, but far-reaching in scope. That he, in a comparatively narrow sphere, should have worked out and foreshadowed the colony plan of the large institutions of today is as marvelous as it is admirable, and history fulfills but a tardy act of justice in placing Guggenbühl's name among those of the pioneers in a work to which he has devoted the best years of his life."

Publications by Guggenbühl

1838: *Der Alpenstich, endemisch im Hochgebirge der Schweiz und seine Verbreitungen.* Mit einem Vorwort von Prof. Troxler. Zürich, S. Höhr.

1840: Hülfsruf aus den Alpen, zur Bekämpfung des schrecklichen Cretinismus. *Malten's Bibliothek der neuesten Weltkunde,* Vo. I, pp. 191 ff.

1841: Europas erste Colonie fur Heilung des Cretinismus auf dem Abendberge im Berner Oberland; und die Versammlung schweizerischer Ärzte und Naturforscher zu Freyburg im August 1840. *Häser's Archiv f.d. ges. Medizin* (Jena), I:293-300.

1844: Über die Heilanstalt am Abendberge. *Ztschr. K. K. Gesellschaft der Ärzte zu Wein,* I, 484-6.

1844: L'Abendberg, établissement pour la guérison et l'éducation des enfants crétins à Interlaken, canton de Berne. Premier rapport. Traduit de l'Allemand sur le manuscript inédit de l'auteur par le dr. Berchtold-Beaupré. Fribourg, Léonce Schmid-Roth.

1844: *Premier rapport sur l'Abendberg*. Fribourg, Léonce Schmid-Roth.

1845: Bericht über die Cretinen-Anstalt auf dem Abendberge. *Verhandlungen der schweizerischen naturforschenden Gesellschaft* (Chur), 1844, 29: 113-29.

1845: Über den Cretinismus und das Hospiz am Abendberge. *Schweiz. Ztschr. für Medizin, Chirurgie und Geburtshilfe (Zürich)*, pp. 109-124.

1846: Briefe über den Abendberg und die Heilanstalt für Cretinismus. Zürich, Orell, Füssli u. Comp.

1851: Sendschreiben an Lord Ashley, Mitglied des Englischen Parlaments, über einige Punkte des öffentlichen Wohles und der christlichen Gesetzgebung. Basel, Bahnmeyers Buchhandlung.

1852: Ein Besuch meiner ausländischen Pflegetöchter. Beobachtungen über den Cretinismus, Tübingen. Drittes Heft, pp. 142-9.

1853: Die Heilung und Verhütung des Cretinismus und ihre neuesten Fortschritte. Mitteilungen an die Schweizerische naturforschende Gesellschaft. Bern und St, Gallen, Huber und Comp.

1860: Die Erforschung des Cretinismus und Blödsinn nach dem jetzigen Zustande der Naturwissenschaften. *Ztschr. d. K. K. Gesellschaft der Ärzte zu Wien*, 16: 84, 104, 116, 136, 170; also published separately: Wien, Ueberreuter.

1862: Über die Notwendigkeit statistischer und ätiologischer Untersuchungen über das Vorkommen des Cretinismus und Idiotismus in Europa und über die Mittel zu deren Verhütung. *Allg. Med. Centr.-Ztg., Berlin*, 31:405-7

Publications about Guggenbühl and the Abendberg

Alther, K. Dr. J. J.: *Guggenbühl und die Anfänge der Schweizerischen Idiotenfürsorge*. St. Gallen, Zollikofersche Buchdruckerei. 1905.

Anonymus: Der Cretinismus und das Hospiz auf dem Abendberg. *Ztschr. f.d. ges. Medizin (Hamburg)*, 29:1-37, 1845

——————: *Du crétinisme, de son historie et de son traitement, avec une notice biographique sur le dr. Guggenbühl*. Genève, F. Ramboz. 1950.

——————: Fragmentarische Notizen über das Cretinen-Institut auf dem Abendberge. *Berner Correspondenz-Blatt fur Ärzte und Apotheker*, 3:97-101, 1852.

————: *Der Abendberg wie er ist.* Eine aktenmässige Beleuchtung der bisherigen Wirksamkeit des Guggenbühl. 23 pp. Bern, J. Gassmann Sohn. 1858.

Auzouy, M.: De l'Abendberg et de Guggenbühl son fondateur. *Ann. méd.-psychol.* (Paris), 4.s.:9, 450-64, 1867.

Brown, B.: The Treatment and Cure of Cretins and Idiots, with an Account of a Visit to the Institution on the Abendberg in Switzerland. *Am. J. M. Sc.,* n.s. 14:109-117, 1847; also Boston, W. T. Tickner, 1847.

Chambers, R. Dr.: Guggenbühl's Hospital for Infant Cretins. *Chambers' Edinburgh Journal, No. 272, May 1848.*

Chavannes, D. A.: Des crétins à l'Abendberg. *Journal de la société vaudoise d'utilité publique* (Lausanne), 1844, No. 145.

Demaria, P. C.: Dei progressi dell'educazione dei cretini ragguaglio tratto da un recente scritto del dottore Guggenbühl. *Giornale delle scienze mediche della Reale Accademia Medico-Chirurgica di Torino.* Fasc. I, 1854.

Demme: Über endemischen Cretinismus. Eigenthum der Rettungsanstalt für Cretinen auf dem Abendberg. Bern. Fischer, 1840.

Fauconneau-Dufresne: Nouvelles de l'établissement de l'Abendberg pour le traitement et l'éducation des crétins. *Union médicale* (Paris). 3:129-31, 1849.

————: Le docteur Guggenbühl et l'Abendberg. *Ibid.,* 1862, 2 s., 14: 65-71.

Forbes, J.: *The Physician's Holiday, or a Month in Switzerland in the Summer of 1848.* London, W. S. Orr. 1850, 3rd ed., 1852.

Froriep, R.: *Die Rettung der Cretinen.* Bern, C. Raetzer. 1856.

Gaussen, L.: *The Abendberg, an Alpine Retreat founded by Dr. Guggenbühl for the Treatment of Infant Cretins.* With an introduction by John Coldstream. Edinburgh, W. P. Kennedy. 1848.

————: *The Wonders of the Abendberg.* (New edition of the above.) Berne, C. Raetzer. 1857.

Gosse, L. A.: Sur le traitement du crétinisme dans l'établissement de l'Abendberg. *Ann. méd.-psych.,* 12:323-46, 1848.

————: *Rapport sur le traitment du créinisme. Genève,* F. Ramboz. 1848.

————: *Extrait des lettres publiées par le docteur Guggenbühl à Zürich. Genève,* F. Ramboz. 1848.

Hahn-Hahn, I.: *Die Kinder auf dem Abendberg*. Berlin, Duncker. 1843.

Helferich, J. H.: (former teacher on the Abendberg). *Das Leben der Cretinen*. Stuttgart. 1850.

Herckenrath, A. W. F.: *Het gesticht voor behoeftige Cretinen-kinderen, opgericht door Dr. Guggenbühl, op den Abendberg, bij Interlaken, in Switzerland, der algemeene belangstelling anbevolen*. Amsterdam. Ten Brink & De Vries, 1842.

Hungerbühler, J. M.: *Bericht sammt Anträgen über die Stiftung für Kretinenkinder auf dem Abendberg*. Bern, November 1850.

Hutchinson, J.: *The Abendberg Hospital for Cretins*. *M. Times & Gaz.* (London), 1855, n. s., 11, 117-9.

Kanner, L.: Johann Jakob Guggenbühl and the Abendberg. *Bull. History Med.*, 33:489-502, 1960.

Nièpce, B.: *Traité du goître et du crétinisme*. Paris, Baillière. 1851.

Potton, A.: L'Abendberg hospice des enfants crétins dans le canton de Berne. *Gazette médicale de Lyon*, 5:1-5, 1833.

Rengger, H. J.: *Guggenbühl, der Bergründer the ersten Heilanstalt für Kretinen und seine Anschauungen über den Kretinismus*. Zürich, Guntzwiller. 1927.

Rösch, C.: *Die Stiftung fur Kretinkinder auf dem Abendberge bei Interlaken in der Schweiz*. Stuttgart, Ebner u. Seubert. 1842.

——————: *Über Heilung und Erziehung unentwickelter oder kretinischer Kinder, mit besonderer Rücksicht auf die Guggenbühlsche Stiftung, etc.* Stuttgart, F. H. Kohler. 1845.

Scoutetten, R. H. J.: *Une visite à l'Abendberg*. Exposé des travaux de la Société des sciences médicales de la Moselle (Metz), 1853, 1-17; 2nd ed., Berne, Raetzer. 1856; 3rd ed. Berne. 1860.

Sengelmann, H.: *Idiotophilus*. Norden, Diedr. Soltau's Verlag. 1885, Vol. I, pp. 68-78.

Twining, W.: *Some Account of Cretinism, and the Institution for its Cure on the Abendberg, near Interlachen, in Switzerland*. London, Parker. 1843.

Valentin: Schreiben über den Abendberg, mit Anmerkungen von Guggenbühl. *Schmidt's Jahrbücher* (Leipzig), 48:270-2, 1845.

Verga, A.: L'Abendberg, Guggenbühl e i cretini. *Gazz. med. ital. lomb.* (Milano), 3.s.:1:353, 368, 1851, 3.s. 2:1, 25, 65, 89, 109, 125, 1850.

Viszanik: *Die Irren-, Heil- und Pflegeanstalten Deutschlands und Frankreichs, sammt der Cretinen-Heilanstalt auf dem Abendberge in der Schweiz*. Wien, C. Gerold. 1845.

Edouard Onesimus Seguin was born January 20, 1812, at Clamecy in France. He attended the Collège d'Auxerre and the Lycée St. Louis in Paris and then studied medicine and surgery under Itard, who encouraged him to devote himself to the investigation and treatment of idiocy. He acknowledged freely his debt to Itard but, probing beyond the matter of individual relationship, saw in his attitude also the result of influences exerted by the "Christian School" or "Saint Simonism," which, in Seguin's own words, was "striving for a social application of the principles of the gospel, for the most rapid evaluation of the lowest and poorest by all means and institutions, mostly by free education."

In those days, he was certainly in need of both an inspiring mentor and a sustaining philosophy. Little support could be expected from the leading alienists. The great Jean Etienne Esquirol, from whom he sought guidance, declared categorically that educational efforts were useless because "no means are known by which a larger amount of reason or intelligence can be bestowed upon the unhappy idiot, even for the briefest period."

Undismayed by such pessimism, Seguin, at twenty-five years of age, made in 1837 an attempt to educate an idiotic boy. He worked with him steadily and strenuously for eighteen months, at the end of which his pupil "was able to make better use of his senses, could remember and compare, speak, write and count." Esquirol was among the first to testify to the success of this venture. On August 18, 1839, he issued a statement in which he gave credit to Seguin, although he subtly defended his own position by referring to the patient as *un enfant . . . semblable à un idiot.*" If we decree that absolutely nothing can be done for an idiot, we can save face by saying that one whose condition has improved must have been a seeming idiot. Nevertheless, Esquirol concluded his statement by endorsing Seguin as a person "capable of giving the educational system all the desirable extension."

Seguin began to treat more' children at the Hospice des Incurables and at the Bicêtre. At the October 12, 1842, session of the administrative council of hospitals in Paris, a commission appointed to report on the results of Seguin's work (under the chairmanship of Dean Orfila of the Faculty of Medicine) reached the following decisions: (1) Seguin should be invited to continue his educational methods which he has so successfully applied at the Hospice des Incurables; (2) The director of the Hospice and the alienists should follow the progress and the results of the methods employed by Seguin. On December 11, 1843, a commission, consisting of Messieurs Serres, Flourens, and Pariset, gave a detailed report of their examination of Seguin's work, which they summed up by stating: "Monsieur Seguin has thus opened up a new career of beneficence. He has given to hygiene, to medicine, to ethics an example worthy of being followed. We, therefore, have the honor of suggesting that a note of thanks be written to Monsieur Seguin for the communication which he has addressed to this Council, and that he be encouraged in his charitable enterprise." In 1844, a commission of the Paris Academy of Sciences, appointed at Seguin's request to examine ten of his pupils, declared that he had definitely solved the problem of idiot education. Seguin, in his later writings, referred to the 1842 and 1843 reports as "the twin cornerstones of all the institutions since founded for the education of idiots."

In 1846, Seguin published his classical textbook, which won immediate recognition, was crowned by the Academy, and brought to its author an autograph letter from Pope Pius IX, thanking him for the services he was rendering to humanity. In this work, Seguin set forth the details of his method of the combined physiological and moral instruction of idiots. "According to this method," Seguin wrote in the introduction to a later book, "education is the ensemble of the means of developing harmoniously and effectively the moral, intellectual and physical capacities, as functions, in man and mankind. To be physiological, education must at first follow the great natural law of action and repose, which is life itself. To adopt this law to the whole training, each function in its turn is called to activity and to rest; the activity of one favoring the repose of the other; the improvement of one reacting upon the improvement of all others; contrast being not only an instrument of relaxation, but of comprehension also . . .The general training embraces the muscular, imitative, nervous, and reflective functions, susceptible of being called into play at any moment."

Seguin's fame spread far and wide, and alienists of many nations flocked to Paris to see the work done by him. But just then came the 1848 revolution and Seguin, distrusting the new regime, packed up and emigrated to the United States. He settled in Cleveland as a general practitioner, then moved to Portsmouth, Ohio. In 1860, after a brief interval as head of the Pennsylvania Training School for Idiots and a visit to his native country, he moved to Mount Vernon, New York. When, in 1861, the medical department of the University of the City of New York conferred on him the M.D. degree, he made his residence in that metropolis, where he spent the last two decades of his life. Since his arrival in this country, he played a major role as consultant to all who were interested in establishing new residential treatment facilities for retarded children or improving those already in existence. He was in contact with Samuel Gridley Howe, whom he visited for two months early in 1852. In 1873, he went to Europe as United States Commissioner on Education at the Vienna Universal Exposition and published a comprehensive report on his impressions of the contemporary ideas about child rearing, school education, and the care of handicapped children.

In 1876, when six men got together to form the Association of Medical Officers of American Institutions for Idiotic and Feeble-Minded Persons, Seguin was chosen as its first president.

The last enterprise of his career was the organization of a Physiological School for Weak-Minded and Weak-Bodied Children in New York City.

As a side interest, Seguin occupied himself with medical thermometry, invented a widely used thermometer, and published several books on the subject; one of them (*Manual of Thermometry for Mothers*, 1875) was written for a lay public.

Seguin died October 28, 1880.

Publications by Seguin

Résumé de ce que nous avons fait pendant quatorze mois. Paris, Porthmann. 1839.

Conseils a M.O. sur l'éducation de son enfant idiot. Paris, Porthmann. 1839.

Théorie et pratique de l'éducation des idiots. Two parts. Paris, Baillière. 1841 and 1842.

Hygiène et éducation des idiots. Paris, Baillière. 1843.

Traitement moral, hygiène et éducation des idiots et des autres enfants arriérés. Paris, Baillière. 1846.

Jacob Rodrigues Pereire, Notice sur sa vie et ses travaux. Paris, Baillière. 1847.

Idiocy and its Treatment by the Physiological Method. New York, W. Wood and Co., 1866. (Reprinted 1907 by Teacher's College, Columbia University).

New Facts and Remarks Concerning Idiocy. New York, W. Wood and Co. 1870.

Family Thermometry; a Manual for Mothers, Nurses, Hospitals, etc. New York, C. P. Putnam. 1875.

The Clinical Thermoscope. New York, Putnam. 1875.

International Uniformity in the Practice and Record of Physic. New York, J. F. Trow. 1876.

Medical Thermometry and Human Temperature. New York, W. Wood & Co. 1876.

Psycho-Physiological Training of an Idiotic Hand. New York, G. P. Putnam's Sons. 1879.

Vienna International Exhibition. 1873. Report on Education. Washington, Government Printing Office, 1875. Second Edition; Milwaukee, Doerflinger. 1880.

Biographical Data About Seguin

Boyd, W. From Locke to Montessori. New York, Henry Holt, 1914. Chapter VI: Eduard Seguin, pp. 88-129.

Dana, C. L. The Seguins of New York, Their Careers and Contributions to Science and Education. Annals of Medical History, New York, 1924, 6, 475-479.

Holman, H. Seguin and His Physiological Method of Education. London, Pitman. 1914.

Kraft, I. Edouard Seguin and the 19th Century Moral Treatment of Idiots. Bull. History Med., 1961, 35, 393-418.

Samuel Gridley Howe. Prior to the 19th Century, there was no public or private facility for the care of retarded children on the North American Continent. A small attempt was made in

1818 to provide a place for a very limited number at the Asylum for the Deaf and Dumb in Hartford, Connecticut.

The idea of a special residential school for the feebleminded in this country stems from Massachusetts. In July 1848, Hervey Backus Wilbur (1820-1883) took into his home at Barre a group of defective children beginning with the seven year old son of a distinguished lawyer. At about the same time, Dr. Samuel

Samuel Gridley Howe in His Early Thirties. Oil Portrait by Jane Stewart. (From Laura E. Richards, Samuel Gridley Howe: *Letters and Journals*. Boston, Dana Estes & Co., 1909.)

Gridley Howe was able to convince his contemporaries that the training and education of the feebleminded was a public responsibility.

Howe, born in 1801, graduated from Harvard Medical School in 1824. He volunteered for six years as a surgeon in the Greek war of liberation. On his return to the United States, he collected sixty thousand dollars which he personally disbursed in a relief depot at Aegina; soon thereafter, he arranged a refugee colony for exiles on the Isthmus of Corinth. At an early time, he developed an enthusiastic interest in blind and deaf children. He made a trip to England in preparation for the founding of a New England Asylum for the Blind. He was temporarily diverted from his purpose when, asked by Lafayette to carry funds to the Polish revolutionaries across the Prussian frontier, he was caught and imprisoned in Berlin. After his release in April 1832, he took a few blind children into his father's house. Colonel Thomas H. Perkins was so impressed that he offered his house and garden on Boston's Pearl Street as a permanent location of what is known as the Perkins Institution for the Blind, which Howe directed until his death in 1876. Howe developed new methods for the instruction of the sightless and deafmutes, and his phenomenal success with one of his pupils, Laura Bridgman (who could neither hear nor see), won him international fame. He was actively associated with Dorothea Lynde Dix in her work for the insane and with Charles Sumner and Horace Mann in the struggle for educational reforms. Together with his wife Julia Ward (they were married on April 27, 1843), he was an advocate of Negro emancipation. In 1866, appalled by the plight of the Cretans, he went back to Greece and established in Athens a school for refugees from the island.

Howe's profound interest in the handicapped did not fail to include the feebleminded. His daughter, Laura E. Richards, wrote: "In the course of his labors and research in behalf of the blind and the insane, especially of the latter, he had been deeply impressed with the sufferings and needs of a kindred class, the idiotic and feebleminded." More specifically, he was led to the first practical steps by his experience with three blind children who were also idiotic and whom he treated "with considerable success." He inferred that, "if so much could be done for idiots who were blind, still more could be done for idiots who were not blind."

Inspired by Howe, Judge Horatio Boyington, then a member of the House of Representatives, moved on January 22, 1846, an order for the appointment of a committee "to consider the expediency of appointing commissioners to inquire into the condition of the idiots of the commonwealth, to ascertain their number and whether anything can be done for their relief, and to report to next General Court." The order was passed and printed on the same day. A report of the committee, presented on March 25, urged the appointment of such commissioners, and on April 11, Judge Boyington, Dr. Howe, and Gilman Kimball were chosen.

In the two years following, those three sent circular letters to town clerks and other responsible persons in every community of the Commonwealth, visited sixty-three towns, and personally examined the status of 574 "human beings who are condemned to hopeless idiocy and left to their own brutishness."

On February 26, 1848, the commissioners submitted their first report, written and signed by Howe as chairman. A few extracts will give its flavor:

"Massachusetts admits the right of all her citizens to a share in the blessings of education; she provides it liberally for all her more favored children; if some be blind or deaf, she still continues to furnish them with special instructions at great cost; and will she longer neglect the poor idiots — the most wretched of all who are born to her, — those who are usually abandoned by their fellows, — who can never, of themselves, step upon the platform of humanity, — will she leave them to their dreadful fate, to a life of brutishness, without an effort in their behalf? . . .

"The benefits to be derived from the establishment of a school for this class of persons, upon humane and scientific principles would be very great. Not only would all the idiots who should be received into it be improved in their bodily and mental condition, but all the others in the State and the country would be indirectly benefited. The school, if conducted by persons of skill and ability, would be a model for others. Valuable information would be disseminated through the country; it would be demonstrated that no idiot need be confined or restrained by force; that the young can be trained for industry, order, and self-respect; that they can be redeemed from odious and filthy habits, and there is not one of any age who may not be made more of a man and less of a brute by patience and kindness directed by energy and skill."

The report made a profound impression. There were a few scoffers, it is true. A caricature was circulated, which represented Sumner and Howe as twin Don Quixotes riding a tilt against various windmills, and one critic remarked: "The doctor's report is one for idiots as well as one concerning them."

Nevertheless, the legislature consented to allow $2,500 per annum for three years for the teaching and training of ten idiotic children. A wing was opened on October 1, 1848, at the Perkins Institution to serve as "an experimental school." A competent teacher was found, James B. Richards, who later did pioneering work in Pennsylvania.

Toward the end of the three years, the Joint Committee of Public Charitable Institutions visited the place, reported that "the experiment seems to have succeeded entirely," and suggested that the school be put on a permanent footing. An institution was incorporated under the name of Massachusetts School for Idiotic and Feeble-Minded Youth. A pleasant site was chosen in South Boston in 1855, and the children were moved thither from the Perkins Institution. Howe made daily rounds, examined all candidates for admission, engaged all officers, and prescribed diets, regimen, rules and regulations, discipline and exercises. In 1887, the school was located permanently in Waltham; it is now known as the Walter E. Fernald State School, in recognition of the long services of one of its most distinguished superintendents.

As Guggenbühl deserves the credit for inaugurating the institutional care of retarded children in Europe, so does the credit go to Howe for rendering the same kind of service in this country. We know that Howe had visited Guggenbühl's Abendberg before he submitted his report in 1848 and that he was full of praise of the Swiss enterprise. We do not know for certain whether he had also been to the Bicêtre (it is certain that his friend Charles Sumner was there) but, when Seguin came to America, Howe invited him to come to Boston. Happily, he wrote to Horace Mann on January 21, 1852: "I have luckily secured

Dr. Seguin, formerly the life and soul of the French school for idiots," and on March 15, 1852, he wrote to Charles Sumner: "Seguin has been here two months, and proves to be a man of great vigor of intellect, and full of resources; he has done wonders — but we can hardly keep him."

Howe kept up his concern for the blind, the deaf, the insane, the feebleminded, the slaves, and the oppressed nations (particularly Greece) to the end of his busy life. Oliver Wendell Holmes wrote a touching "Memorial Tribute" to Howe in beautiful verse, from which these lines are taken:

"He touched the eyelids of the blind,
And lo, the veil withdrawn,
As o'er the midnight of the mind
He led the light of dawn."

Publications by Howe

Report made to the Legislature of Massachusetts on Idiocy. Boston, Collidge & Wiley. 1848.

Report to Inquire into the Condition of Idiots of the Commonwealth of Massachussetts, No. 51, February 28, 1948.

Second Annual Report of the Doings under the Resolves of the Legislature, May 8, 1948, for Training and Teaching Idiots, January 20, 1851, Senate No. 9, Boston. 1851.

Third and Final Report of the Experimental School. *American Journal of Insanity*, 1852, 9, 20.

A Letter to the Governor of Massachussetts upon His Veto of a Bill Providing for an Increase of State Beneficiaries at the School of Idiotic Children. Boston, Tickner and Fields. 1857.

On the Causes of Idiocy. Edinburgh, McLachlan and Stewart. 1858. (Contains an abstract of the first report, the entire supplement, 12 of the original 47 pages of tables, and 20 pages of appendix: excerpts from later reports by Howe.)

Biographical Data on Howe

Harrington, T. F. Samuel Gridley Howe. *In* The Harvard Medical School. New York & Chicago, Lewis Publishing Co. 1905, Vol. II, pp. 741-753.

Haskell, R. H.: An Apostrophy to the Memory of a Noble American. *Am. J. Mental. Deficiency, 49*:358-363, 1944-5.

Phalen, J. M.: Dr. Samuel Gridley Howe, a Yankee Cervantes. *Military Surgeon, 88*:553-555, 1941.

Richards, Laura E. (Howe's Daughter): *Letters and Journals of Samuel Gridley Howe.* Boston, Dana Estes & Co. 1909. Two volumes.

————: *Samuel Gridley Howe.* New York. Appleton-Century. 1935. *Am. J. Ment. Deficiency, 49*:358-363, 1944-5.

Schwartz, H.: *Samuel Gridley Howe, Social Reformer.* Cambridge, Harvard Univ. Press. 1956.

Williams, F. E.: Dr. Samuel G. Howe and the Beginnings of Work for the Feebleminded in Massachussetts, *Boston Medical and Surgical Journal, 177*:481-484, 1917.

Chapter 3

The Era of Institutional Expansion

GUGGENBÜHL'S VENTURE had kindled a spark which, regardless of the sad fate of the Abendberg itself, spread quickly over Europe and the North American Continent. The idea and practice of consistent training of *individual* mental defectives had been given impetus by Itard and refined by Seguin. The idea and practice of the institutional training of *groups* of children with a combined emphasis on medicine and education originated with Guggenbühl.

It would be historically incorrect to say that the Abendberg represented the first gathering together of defective children in one locality set aside for them. There were a few "asylums," providing not more than attention to primitive physical needs and connected either with hospitals or churches. A small such ward existed at the hospital at Sitten in Wallis, another in Chur in the canton of Graubünden. An *Erziehungsanstalt für stumpfsinnige Kinder* is said by Kirmsse to have been started by a Dr. Schnell in Wiflisburg (Canton of Waadt). Occasionally, a few cretins were admitted to a church-sponsored place in Graz, Styria. A religious foundation (*Stiftung*) cared since 1828 for twelve cretins at Admont, also in Styria; this extremely wealthy Benedictine monastery, in which the patients were kept, came to a tragic end on April 27, 1865, when for several days it was burned to the ground and seven people perished in a fire set by one of the cretins. (In 1861, in the same place, two cretins and a deafmute had murdered an invalid idiot on whom they took revenge "because he had received an extra bowl of soup from the cook." The two cretins were held responsible and sentenced, the deaf-mute went free because he was held not responsible (*unzurech-nungsfähig*).

A teacher in Salzburg was the first to introduce the idea of mental training in Austria; he started the nucleus of an institution which, lacking official and financial support, was closed in 1835. Little is known about his effort. Biographical data are not available. It is impossible to ascertain the given name of the man. Even the last name has been spelled differently by those who mentioned him and his ventures: Guggenmoos, Goggenmos, Goggenmoos. Some say that he started an institution (also called a school) for cretins in 1816, according to others it was opened in 1818 or in 1828. He himself has left no written notes. The Austrian Regierungsrat J. J. von Knolz reminisced in 1852 that Guggenmoos had achieved "phenomenal success with his human endeavors." (Wiener medizinische Wochenschrift 1852, 2, 193-200.)

In the year in which Guggenmoos was forced to abandon his labors, Pastor Haldenwang of Wildberg in Württemberg took a number of idiotic children ("cretins") into his residence. For twelve years, he tried to befriend them and give them some training. Just when, because of lack of support, he was forced to give up completely, Mariaberg was opening its doors (in 1847) and accepted ten children from Wildberg among its first thirteen inmates.

Those were the few forerunners of the big movement inaugurated by Guggenbühl. It had seemed for a while that the big push would come from France.

FRANCE

Paris had two huge receptacles for all those who had fallen by the wayside because of extreme poverty, mental illness, blindness, senility, epilepsy, prostitution, invalidism, and mental deficiency: Bicêtre and the Salpêtrière.

Bicêtre was a village near the capital city, which was named after a castle built 1285 by Jean de Pontoise, Bishop of Winchester, then Wicestre, and finally corrupted to Bicêtre. In 1346, it passed to the domain of the royal house. In 1411, it was destroyed by fire. King Louis III rebuilt it, enlarged the grounds and intended it as a home for invalid soldiers. In 1656, Louis XIV turned it into a general hospital. For a time it served as a "hospice" for indigents, a house of correction, and a home for the aged and chronically ill. Later, a separate section was set aside as the mental hospital for the Départment de la Seine.

The Salpétrière, founded in Aprli 27, 1654, was opened on May 1, 1657, as a general asylum for the impecunious of Paris. Built by the architect Bryant on orders from the President of parliament, Pomponne de Baillière, it derives its name from the fact that it was located on the site of Rue Poliveau where saltpeter had been previously prepared. In 1778, it housed about 8,000 persons, including all forms of human illness, misery, and degeneracy.

It was in these two places that the first primitive attempts were made in France to take in mental defectives. Guillaume Marie André Ferrus, born 1784, who began to study medicine at fourteen years of age, received his doctorate at twenty, and served in Napoleon's armies, was invited by Pinel to join his staff. In 1826, he was named physician-in-chief of the Bicêtre "hospice des aliénés." In 1828, he formed a separate section for idiots and imbeciles. However, in 1835, he was given a task of great national importance, the job of inspector general of his country's mental institutions, and thus lost direct contact with the department which he had created. He had been joined in 1831 by Auguste Felix Voisin who, born in 1794, studied under Esquirol and succeeded Ferrus at Bicêtre. Not too happy about prevailing conditions there, Voisin founded in 1834 a private school at Issy, which he called "orthophrenic" and of which he became the "medical, hygienic, and physiologic" director. He failed to get adequate public support and the Issy establishment remained an ephemeral affair. In 1839, he enlarged the division at Bicêtre. His efforts were continued for a time by the teacher, Vallée, "along the lines worked out by Seguin," who in 1837 had been invited to demonstrate his methods. Vallée opened a private school near Paris in 1848.

1831

At the Salpétriére, a section for idiotic women was started on March 30, 1831, by Jean Pierre Falret. Falret, born 1794, began to study medicine at sixteen years, came in 1811 to Paris, and in 1814 became an assistant of Esquirol at an aid station improvised for soldiers maimed during the war. Little can be said about any progress at this division for mentally defective females. It was described by visitors as an *"habitation plus funeste"* (a most deadly abode).

It is not too difficult to understand why these pioneering attempts which preceded Guggenbühl's by a number of years failed to stir the public imagination. The innovators, Ferrus, Voisin, and Falret, gave most of their time to general psychiatry; the interest in mental defectives, no matter how genuine, was but a sideline and a way station to wider activity. It was Seguin, the only one of his countrymen, remaining enthusiastically faithful to his objective for the rest of his life, who, in the words of Esquirol, had "removed the mark of the beast from the forehead of the idiot." It was another Frenchman, Binet, who almost three-quarters of a century later, made a monumental contribution to the study of the mentally retarded. Yet, the first French attempts fizzled out to the extent that as late as in 1878, Bourneville, in a report about the section for defective children at Bicêtre, called it with disgust *"une situation véritablement honteuse"* (a truly disgraceful situation). In 1885, France still had no other public facilities for defective children than Bicêtre and the Salpétrière, and even these were extremely limited.

(Robert Scoutetten, president of the Société des Sciences medicales de la Moselle, wrote in 1856: *"Comment se fait-il-que la France, si sympathique à toutes les infortunes, n'ait point encore fait d'efforts pour se placer a la hauteur de Wurtemberg, du Piemont, de l'Angleterre et des autres pays?"*)

Private places did not fare better in France for a long time. It was not until 1854 that a French musician, lover of horses, and soldier turned theologian (ordained in 1844) founded an orphanage, called "famille évangélique" at Laforce. Jean Bost, born 1817, took in seventy-five orphan girls. A woman left a neglected idiotic child at his doorsteps and departed. Soon another idiotic child came to his attention. Since these two girls had no proper place in the orphanage, Bost took them into his home. On November 15, 1855, he opened an asylum (Bethesda) with five girls. In September 1858, he founded one (Shiloh) for boys. In 1862 and 1863, he added two homes for epileptic boys and girls (Ebenezer and Bethel). Bost died in 1881.

Guggenbühl seemed to sense that the time was ripe for more than just founding a school. He thundered his message and started a movement. After millennia of inactivity, the second half of the 1840's and the following decades witnessed the opening of one institution after another. As Seguin put it once: "At certain times and eras, the whole race of man, as regards the discovery of truth, seems to arrive at once at a certain point."

Here and there a physician, a teacher, or a clergyman started with modest means, taking a few defective children into his own residence or into a small building rented or bought with funds obtained from charitable donations. Almost invariably, there was a quick expansion — more admissions, larger quarters, additional personnel. Individual efforts began to be recognized by the official authorities; some of the new establishments received either an overall stipend from their governments or per capita contributions for the indigent patients. On some occasions, the officials themselves were instrumental in encouraging and fostering accommodations for the care and training of mental defectives.

It is fascinating to see how, within a span of a few years, there was the same kind of stirring in several countries.

GERMANY

1845

Carl Wilhelm Saegert, director of the Institution for Deaf-mutes in Berlin, felt sorry for those applicants who were denied admission because of mental deficiency. He took it upon himse'f to train one such boy. Encouraged by his results, he brought the issue to the attention of the authorities. He gained the support of Secretary von Eichhorn, who could offer no governmental assistance but allowed Saegert to treat idiotic children on a private basis. Saegert opened the *Heil-und Bildungsanstalt für Blödsinnige zu Berlin* on April 1, 1845 in a small building adjacent to his school for deafmutes. There were fifty pupils in 1848, divided into several groups graded in keeping with justifiable expectations. Later, the place was taken over by Friedrich Heyer, who received his medical degree in 1858. Eventually, the growing institution was transferred to Neustadt-Eberswalde near Berlin.

1845

Schreiberhau in Silesia had since 1835 a small home (*Rettungshaus*) for underprivileged children. In 1845, the owner of a nearby estate asked for the admission of an idiotic child. Once a start had been made, two other feebleminded boys and one girl were accepted in the same year. Others were added from time to time. This never became a regular institution. There were twenty-seven idiots at the place in 1882.

1846

A lecture delivered in 1844 by Ettmüller in Freiberg at a meeting of the *Verein für die Staatsarzneikunde im Königreich Sachsen* so impressed the Ministry of the Interior and Education that it ordered a census of mental defectives to be taken by the district authorities. A teacher was commissioned to observe the work of the few existing institutions. In August 1846, an *experimental school* for ten boys was opened at Hubertusburg. In 1852, it was made into a permanent institution for thirty boys. In 1857, it was made available for both sexes. There were forty-six pupils in 1877, 550 pupils in 1899.

1847

Karl Ferdinand Kern (1814-1868), a teacher, prepared himself for the instruction of deafmutes in Weimar and in Leipzig. In 1839, he founded a similar institution in his native town, Eisenach, where he also treated mental defectives. He became so interested in the latter aspect of his work that he resigned his position and in 1847 started a private school for idiots in Leipzig, moved it in 1854 to Gohlis and in 1859 to Möckern. Feeling that medical knowledge was essential for his activities, he studied medicine and received his degree in 1852, on the basis of his dissertation: *De fatuitatis cura medica et paedagogica consocianda*. His son-in-law, Kind, who collaborated with him for a time, took over the school in Langenhangen in 1868.

1847

Wilhelm I, King of Württemberg, after a tour of the Abendberg, commissioned Dr. Heinrich Karl Rösch to organize an institution, using the Abendberg as a model. A former convent was set aside for the purpose and became, as Mariaberg, on May 1, 1847, the first government-sponsored German center for the care of idiotic children.

The convent had been built by Count Hugo von Montfort whose two children had run out to play and disappeared. The Count vowed to give a church to the Virgin Mary if the children were found. Their bodies were discovered in a shed and their father kept his promise. In the course of time, poor upkeep brought the buildings so close to ruin that the nuns left it and it stood unoccupied. The king turned the structures and their spacious grounds over to Rösch.

The new institution was opened with thirteen children, ten of whom had been transfered from Pastor Haldenwang's place in Wildberg, which had not been able to maintain itself. Queen Olga was its patroness, and among the prominent people on its board of advisers were the psychiatrists Autenrieth and Griesinger.

Rösch, born at Waldbach in Württemberg in 1808, was a dedicated man. With the assistance of the resident physician, Dr. Krais, he worked incessantly to create a humane, medically oriented *Heilanstalt*. His eager devotion and untiring insistence on improvements and expansion of the facilities incurred the displeasure of the ruling clique, as did his liberal ideas. He was asked to resign from the directorship of Mariaberg and was given the less conspicuous job of public health officer in the small community of Gaildorf. But Rösch could not stand the political reaction which followed the 1848 upheaval in Central Europe. He decided to leave Germany and came to the United States, where he settled near St. Louis. He died December 13, 1866.

After he left Mariaberg, he was succeeded by Authenrieth as head of the board and Karl Zimmer became the resident physician.

1849

Two inmates were the first occupants of an institution opened on May 21, 1849, at Rieth in Württemberg in a rented castle. Two years later, as many as fifty-one children were cared for. In 1851, enough money from private contributions was available to purchase at Winterbach a place which had previously served as a summer resort. The number of patients kept increasing and more spacious accommodations were needed. A munificent gift in the will of Count Alexander Emil von Wartensleben made it possible to acquire the castle Stetten near Canstatt with all of its buildings and a large park. In 1866, a full-time physician was employed. An attempt to have a vocational training school as a part of the institution had to be given up because of the difficulty of obtaining skilled teaching personnel.

1849

Dr. C. F. Hansen invested his own savings in a place for mentally defective children at Eckernförde in the then Danish province of Schleswig. When everything was ready for the reception of patients, a fire destroyed the premises. Hansen, undaunted, started all over again and, though crippled by a severe diplegia, established an institution with eleven children in the city of Schleswig. The Danish government encouraged the admission of poor patients at the expense of their communities. There were forty-five inmates in 1860. After Hansen's death in 1861, his widow took over; she soon transferred the ownership to a Dr. Stender. On August 3, 1862, the institution was moved to Sonderburg, where it experienced great hardship during the Danish war with Prussia and Austria in 1864. The director reported: "During the siege, the bullets which turned half of the city to ashes and ruins drove us out and we were forced to find refuge in the barns of a farm. We had an epidemic of diphtheria and typhoid fever. The director's wife, all of the personnel, and one-third of the children became ill. There was no instruction for a whole year. In July, the buildings of the

institution were sufficiently restored to make our return possible."
On July 19, 1870, at the start of the Franco-Prussian war, the
institution was moved back to the city of Schleswig, with the
permission of the Prussian Government. It remained for a long
time a private enterprise with governmental support.

1852

An Association for the Foundation and Maintenance of an
Institution for Cretins, inspired by the priest Joseph Probst,
opened on October 17, 1852, a Heilanstalt with fourteen children
in Ecksberg, Bavaria, under the protectorate of Archbishop
Carl August von München-Freysing.

1854

Another clergyman, Conrad Wilhelm Löhe (1808-1872),
who was active in founding hospitals, schools, and missions,
rented on May 9, 1854, a few rooms in the upper story of an
inn for the care of a defective child. When within a year the
number went up to eighteen, he moved them to larger
quarters. Eventually, these also proved insufficient, and a
spacious institution was erected at Neuendettelsau.

1859

F. Barthold was made the director of a school begun on
January 17, 1859, at München-Gladbach for defective children of
the Rhineland and Westphalia, with the participation of the
churches, the government, and civic organizations.

1861

Marie von Nathusius, the popular writer of pious stories,
did not rest until two institutions were started in the Harz
region, one for girls at Hasserode and one for boys in the small
village of Neinstedt.

1862

Six children formed the nucleus of a private enterprise in
Kiel, undertaken by an interested citizen, Johannes Meyer.
Though there were some governmental contributions and donations came from the Association of Volunteer Friends of the
Poor, the place was in constant financial plight. Nonetheless,
the number of patients grew to 100 in the first ten years of
its existence.

1862

Count Adalbert von der Recke-Volmerstein (1791-1876) devoted the major part of his life to philanthropy. He was interested in supporting Sunday Schools, alleviating the lot of prison inmates, and in extending a helping hand to anyone in any kind of need. He announced in March 1860 his plan to build a Samaritan asylum at Craschnitz near Düsseldorf for the reception of incurable, sick, paralyzed, crippled, blind, and feeble-minded children. King Frederick Wilhelm IV of Prussia made a substantial contribution, Napoleon III sent 1,000 francs, and donations came from England. The institution was opened in 1862, probably the only one in history which, without any pretense at specialization, aimed at extending help to children with all and every kind of malady or anomaly.

1862

A school was opened in Langenhangen, Hanover, with thirty inmates. In 1868, its direction was taken over by Karl Friedrich Kind (born 1825), who had begun his professional career as a teacher, became associated with Kern at Möckern, acquired a medical degree in 1860, and established in 1866 an office as a general practitioner at Grimma. Between 1868 and his death on October 15, 1884, he was not only an able administrator but one of the leaders in efforts directed toward institutional reforms. When he took charge, the place had 170 pupils. In 1902, there were 709 patients (of whom 151 were epileptics), twenty-eight buildings, two hospitals, and a school of ten classes.

1863

Pastor Martin Heinrich Sengelmann was a very active and enterprising man. His interests went in many directions, all converging on the education of children and adolescents. In 1850, he started a vocational school. To this he added on October 19, 1863, an asylum for feebleminded children in Alsterdorf near Hamburg. Sengelmann's interests in the care of mental defectives went far beyond the attention to this enterprise. He was responsible for calling together the first conference of directors of the German institutions for mental defectives.

There was obviously no halting the trend toward the establishment of institutions for mentally defective children. There were more than thirty in Germany by 1885, about 100 in

1917. In a relatively small number did the impetus come from physicians. In most instances, religious sentiments, rather than medical curiosity and zeal, were the guiding principles. The men most active and influential were clergymen, leading among whom were Sengelmann, whose "Idiotophilus" (*Systematic Textbook of the Care of Idiots*) is a valuable source book for anyone interested in the history of mental deficiency, and the pastor Julius Disselhoff, whose book on the conditions of cretins, mental defectives, and idiots in the Christian countries (1857) was read widely and served as inspiration for many of those who were influential in swaying the public.

GREAT BRITAIN — ENGLAND

Guggenbühl can be said to be the godfather of the institutional care of feebleminded children in Great Britain. Twining's visit to the Abendberg in 1842 and his glowing report in 1843 created a stir which was to keep many philanthropists and personages in high places in constant agitation.

1846

Inspired by Twining's report, the Misses White started in 1846 a small school with four children at Bath on the Avon. This developed into the Rock Hall House School under the trusteeship of the Municipal Charities of Bath, which was later amalgamated with the Magdalen Hospital. This hospital owed its establishment to an ancient charity founded in the 17th Century as a leper hospital in connection with the Priory Chapel of St. Mary Magdalen: "Probably, as the demand for accommodation of lepers diminished, lunatics and idiots took their place. Thus, the Bath institution may claim, by right of succession, to be the most ancient foundation in Great Britian for the mental defectives, and it is on record that 'idots' were in residence at the Magdalen Hospital early in the 18th Century" (Shuttleworth and Potts).

In 1847, a personal inspection of the Abendberg was made by Andrew Reed (1787-1862), a nonconformist divine and philanthropist, ordained minister in 1811, who had founded three orphan asylums (on a non-denominational basis) and a home for incurables. He also visited Saegert in Berlin and Seguin in

Paris. In his efforts to do something for the care of feebleminded children, Reed was supported by John Conolly (1794-1866), the superintendent of the psychiatric hospital at Hanwell, and by Samuel Gaskell, Commissioner of Lunacy, who publicized the work of Seguin. At Reed's instigation, at a meeting on October 27, 1847, at which the Lord Mayor of London presided, a committee was constituted to work for the establishment of a public institution, with the motto: "We plead for those who cannot plead for themselves."

1848

On April 26, 1848, such a place was inaugurated at Park House, Highgate, under the sponsorship of the Duke of Cambridge. Guggenbühl was invited to England to give advice. His visit, as Twining wrote, "has caused fresh observations on the subject to be made known and confined." Gaskell, in a talk before the British Association for the Advancement of Natural Sciences, pointed to the glorious example of the Abendberg and asked for more institutions. In 1848, Forbes reported: "I was fortunate enough to enter into a conditional agreement with one of Guggenbühl's Sisters of Charity to come to England to assist in conducting the business of the Asylum for Idiots lately instituted and now in active operation at Highgate." Highgate had fifty pupils at the end of the first year.

In 1851, Guggenbühl, in an open letter (*Sendschreiben*) to Lord Ashley, Member of Parliament, urged "that the matter be made the subject of legislative procedure." As a direct result, the care of feebleminded children became a governmental concern in England.

1855

On April 15, 1855, the Highgate institution was moved to Earlswood near Red Hill, in Surrey as the receiving place for the Northern Counties. The cornerstone had been laid on June 16, 1852, by Prince Albert.

1859

Another portion of the Highgate inmates was transferred in 1859 to Essex Hall near Colchester, a large new home with ample grounds donated by Samuel Morton Peto, for the Eastern Counties.

It was during the time of his affiliation with Earlswood that J. Langdown Down presented in 1866 his description of what is now known as mongolism.

Other schools followed in quick succession: Star Cross, Exeter, in 1864; the Royal Albert Asylum for the Western Counties, Lancaster, in 1864; Knowle, opened at Birmingham for the Midland Counties in 1866.

SCOTLAND

1854

Sir John and Lady Jane Ogilvy had had their own mentally defective child at the Abendberg. They were so pleased that they decided to have a similar institution in their own country. They founded one in 1854 at their estate in Baldovan near Dundee and placed it under the jurisdiction of the Board of Lunacy for Scotland.

1855

Dr. Brodie (author of *The Education of the Imbecile and the Improvement of Invalid Youth.* 1856) opened a small school at Larbert near Falkirk. It was there that Dr. William Ireland did a major part of the work which made his textbook possible.

1867

Columbia Lodge near Edinburgh was started in 1867.

IRELAND

1869

When the Census Commissioners reported 7,033 defectives in 1861, they suggested that steps be taken similar to those in England and on the Continent. In 1869, the Stewart Institution was opened at Palmerston with forty-three pupils.

THE NETHERLANDS

1855-(1857)

An enthusiastic account of his visit to the Abendberg by Herckenrath, published in Amsterdam in 1842, prompted the Queen of the Netherlands to make a personal journey to Guggenbühl's show place. With the aid of the court preacher,

Cornelius Eliza von Koetsvelt, the queen was instrumental in opening on May 15, 1855, a day school for "educable" retarded children with twenty-one boys and ten girls. After many conferences with a number of initially reluctant governmental agencies, it was possible to start in 1857 a residential place at the Hague for seventy children.

SWITZERLAND

1857-(1867)

After the ignominious collapse of Guggenbühl's Abendberg, there must have been among his countrymen a considerable cooling off of the original jubilation about the great expectations from the institutional care of mental defectives. It was not until May, 1857, when the subject was brought up again. Dr. C. G. Jung advocated an asylum for feebleminded children at the session of a philanthropic society in Basel. Dr. Jung placed a five-franc piece on the table and said: "With this coin I am founding an institution for backward children." He rented a house, secured a director, his relatives contributed the furnishings, and a month later the place was opened with three children. When there were ten, the space was inadequate and the children were moved to a somewhat larger locale. Jung died on June 20, 1864. A committee created by him continued the work and acquired a large estate which opened its doors in October 1867.

1868

Pastor Appenzeller, with the help of a charitable society, started an institution for thirty children at Weissenheim near Berne.

In 1902, Switzerland had eighteen institutions, all private, some few receiving state appropriations.

THE SCANDINAVIAN COUNTRIES – DENMARK

1855

J. R. Hübertz visited the Abendberg in 1852 under the sponsorship of Queen Dowager Caroline Amalie of Denmark, who was impressed by his statistical study published in the preceding year. His efforts resulted in the purchase of a farm,

Gamble Bakkehus, near Copenhagen for a small private institution opened on November 1, 1855, with Pastor H. P. Duurloo as its first director. The place received a subvention from the Ministry of Public Education.

1856

Johann Keller (1830-1884), a graduate theologian intensely interested in the instruction of deafmutes, started in 1856 a small private school in a garret. He lived to establish five different institutions, three for deafmutes, one for teachable defectives, and one for idiots. After his death, the schools for deafmutes were taken over by the government, while those for the feeble-minded remained the property of the family, with Keller's physician son, Christian, as director. His establishment had six separate divisions.

1. The school proper.
2. A department for feeblemined men able to work.
3. An industrial section for feebleminded women.
4. A home for epileptic children.
5. A home for low-grade defective children.
6. An asylum for adult idiots.

There was enough public interest in the country to lead to the foundation of the Society for the Friends of the Schools for the Abnormal, with headquarters in Copenhagen.

NORWAY

1877

While public conscience was awakened by Dr. Ludwig Dahl's eloquent writings, it was not until 1876 that anything of practical significance was attempted. An experiment to attach an instructional unit to the public school system proved inadequate. A private school, with state support for indigents was opened in 1877, with separate divisions for boys and for girls. In 1881, a law was enacted which made the training of all "idiots capable of learning" obligatory. Toward the end of the 19th Century, Norway and Saxony were the only European countries where education was compulsory alike for normal and abnormal children.

SWEDEN

1863-1878

The army chaplain Glasell started the first Swedish institution in 1863. Emanuella Carlbeck, who conducted it for a time, opened one of her own at Sköfde with governmental participation. An Association for the Education of Feebleminded Children was instrumental in establishing one in Stockholm in 1878. By 1885, Sweden had eleven institutions with a total of 220 inmates; all of them had women as superintendents. By 1904, there were thirty-three institutions in Sweden.

AUSTRO-HUNGARIAN MONARCHY—AUSTRIA

1864

An official visit to the Abendberg by Count Bombelles, the Austrian minister to Switzerland, directed the attention of his countrymen to the necessity of taking a census and making some provisions for idiots. Guggenbühl himself added an appeal to the Viennese Academy of Science, and a school for idiots was built on the grounds of the mental hospital at Ybbs in 1864.

1871

The St. Anna Women's Organization founded an institution with a capacity for 300 children in Prague. This school was under the direction of Dr. Karl Amerling, head of the Bohemian Physiocratic Society and founder of an abstruse doctrine which went by the name of "diasophy."

1879

The Pius Institute at Bruck in Styria owed its existence to the activities of the Congregation of the Sisters of the Holy Cross.

1883

An "Association for the Establishment of an Asylum for the Education and Welfare of Feebleminded Children" opened on November 28, 1883, the Stephanie Institution, named for the then Crown Princess, at Biedermannsdorf near Vienna, under the direction of Anton Antensteiner.

HUNGARY

1875

Starting with one patient, a commission created an institution which had the name "Arbeit" (Work). In 1877, having as many as nine pupils, it was moved to Villa Weiss in Budapest, under the direction of a Dr. Frim. In 1879, this was the only place for retarded children in Hungary which at that time is said to have had 18,351 "idiots and cretins," of whom 7,970 were of school age. "Arbeit" had then exactly thirteen inmates.

EASTERN EUROPE — RUSSIA AND POLAND

Though there is little specific information available about the care of retarded children in the Slav countries of Eastern Europe, all sources agree that on the whole they were treated humanely. Wollen wrote: "From the 13th Century, town councils in Poland and Russia took over the care of the mentally ill and infirm who were nursed in the hospitals by untrained women and separated from other patients. They were never cruelly treated and there was no demonological approach to the mental defect . . . always recognized as some form of illness." In the mental hospitals, started in Poland in the 17th and in Russia in the 18th Century, idiots in need of hospitalization were housed together with psychotics. In Russia, there were, besides the hospitals, "work houses" for the indigents; in those, by a decree of June 2, 1859, one hundred places were made available for incurables and idiots.

LATVIA
1854

Freidrich Platz, a teacher of deafmutes, opened an "institution for remedial education" in Riga. After his death ten years later, his widow, Therese, was in charge. A number of her publications appeared in German language periodicals. The school had twelve inmates in 1876, twenty-eight in 1885.

FINLAND
1876

M. K. Lundberg started a small private school at Jacobstad with nine pupils, with some state support. This led in 1883 to the establishment of special state schools. In 1890, Edwin Hedman opened a private school in Helsingfors (Helsinki) for sixty pupils under state patronage.

THE UNITED STATES OF AMERICA

1848

Institutional care of retarded children in this country began, of course, with Howe's few patients at the Perkins Institute in Boston, as described in detail in the second chapter. Howe's activities on behalf of the feebleminded were not confined to his home state. He and Seguin, who came to the United States in 1848, were helpful to those who were engaged in the organization of similar enterprises.

In the forty years since the first step was undertaken by Howe in Massachusetts, fifteen places opened their doors to mental defectives, one in each of fourteen states, two in New York. They were variously called school, training school, asylum, home, institute, or institution. In practically all instances, the stimulus came from medical men, while in the European countries it came much more frequently from non-medical sources.

In New York, Dr. Frederick Backus of Rochester introduced at the 1846 session of the legislature a bill for the opening of a residential school; it was passed in one house but failed to carry in the other chamber. In the winter of 1850-51, Howe appeared with some of his patients before the state authorities at Albany, showing what he had done in Massachusetts, and pleading for the establishment of a similar school in New York. Governor Hunt wrote to him in July, 1851: "Your visit to our capital last winter was of great service. We feel that we are much indebted to you for the success of the measure so far, and hope we may have the benefit of your experience and counsel in carrying our plan into practical operation."

1851

In the same year, a school was opened at Albany with Dr. Henry B. Wilbur as its first superintendent; it was moved to Syracuse in 1855. The initial budget amounted to $6,000 annually for two years. Starting as an "experimental school," the place was named State Asylum for Idiots when permanency was secured and later was known officially as the Syracuse State Institution for the Feeble-Minded.

Wilbur had decided in 1848 to take into his own home at Barre, Mass., the retarded seven year old son of a distinguished lawyer. This act led quickly to the start of a Private Institution for the Education of Feeble-Minded Children, "designed for the education and managmeent of all children who by reason of mental infirmity are not fit subjects for ordinary school instruction."

After a public school had been decided on at Albany, "a part of the committee appointed to select a superintendent teacher repaired to Barre, in Massachusetts, where a private school for the training and instruction of idiots had been maintained for more than three years by Henry B. Wilbur. Their object was to become acquainted with a subject so novel to us, in order to qualify them to decide on the qualifications necessary for the principal teacher. They found the school in such admirable condition, they had such evidence of the great capacity of Dr. Wilbur, of his devotedness to a wearisome and trying labor, from which most men of refinement and education would recoil, and of his great success, that they determined on an effort to induce him to leave his very profitable school, and take charge of the proposed asylum for this State." The act establishing the school limited the number of pupils to twenty. (First Annual Report of the Trustees of the New York State Asylum for Idiots to the Legislature of the State, in Senate February 9, 1852.)

The private school at Barre was continued under the directorship of Dr. George Brown, whose reports (printed by J. H. Goddard, Barre, Mass.) are stylistic masterpieces. An article by a visitor to the place and published in the February, 1870 issue of *Appleton's Journal* described the school and its management in truly dithyrambic terms.

Wilbur presided over the Syracuse institution until his death in 1883. He was succeeded by J. C. Carson, who resigned in 1912. Under the next superintendent, O. H. Cobb, the school in Syracuse became one "exclusively for boys and girls of the higher grades," those "for custodial care" being admitted to Newark (established 1873) and Rome (est. 1894).

1853

Pennsylvania came next. The Fifteenth Annual Report of the Pennsylvania Training School for Feebleminded Children (Philadelphia, Ashmead. 1868) gave this brief statement about "origin and plan": "On the tenth of February, 1853, the preliminary steps were taken to found the third Institution of its kind in America, and on the seventh day of April, A.D. 1853, our Legislature incorporated the Pennsylvania Training School for Feebleminded Children, and took it under fostering care, by which, with the liberality of our citizens, and the blessings of Providence, it now ranks first in our Union for architectural size and number of inmates."

James B. Richards, "a teacher who had had experience as an assistant of Howe," was placed in charge as "Principal." In 1855, a house was purchased on Woodbine Avenue in Germantown, chosen because of its "retiredness, accessibility and healthfulness." Even though it was meant to be permanent, enlargement was called for and, under the superintendency of Dr. Joseph Parrish, the school was moved to Elwyn, near Media. It is now known as the Elwyn Training School, named after Dr. Alfred L. Elwyn, a well-known Philadelphia physician.

The school had three departments: Hospital, school, and industrial. There were six ways of obtaining admission: From a state fund of Pennsylvania, one each of New Jersey, Delaware, and Maryland, a City of Philadelphia Fund, soldier's orphans of Pennsylvania, and "pay list" of private patients. At the beginning of the Civil War, there were about a dozen children from "the States in rebellion." It was next to impossible to obtain payments from the parents of seven pupils who remained at Elwyn. Bishop Alonzo Potter, president of the board, reporting on January 3, 1865, to the Senate and House of Representatives, wrote: "This encumbrance remains a serious drawback upon the Institution, but humanity dictates a continuance of the forbearing policy hitherto adopted."

When Dr. Parrish resigned in 1864 to assume duties with the Sanitary Commission to "administer to the sick and wounded soldiery," he was succeeded by his former assistant, Dr. Isaac N. Kerlin. Kerlin (1834-1893) had studied medicine at the

University of Pennsylvania and joined the Elwyn staff in 1858. In 1862, he enlisted in the Army, served in an "impoverished hospital" at Hagerstown, Md., and in the Army of the Potomac in Suffolk, Va., where his work with Negro refugees attracted attention.

Kerlin was active not only locally as an excellent administrator but on a much wider scale in furthering the cause of retarded children. It was he who initiated the idea of forming an association of superintendents of the existing institutions. He fostered occupational training at Elwyn. In 1889, he had sterilization of patients performed with the parents' consent. In 1892, shortly before his death, he was elected President of the American Association on Mental Deficiency.

1857

An Institution of Feebleminded Youth at Columbus, Ohio, was called into existence by legislative enactment on April 17, 1857. The main and central buildings were swept by fire on November 18, 1881, with no lives lost. Dr. G. A. Doren was the first superintendent.

1858

The first school for retarded children in Connecticut was begun owing to the efforts of Dr. Henry M. Knight. Knight, born August 11, 1827, at Stafford Conn., graduated in 1849 from Berkshire Medical College at Pittsfield, Mass., and went into general practice. In 1854, he was elected to the State Legislature and, on his initiative, was appointed on a committee to ascertain the number of imbecile children in the state. They were found to be "as numerous as the insane, eight times as numerous as the deaf and dumb, and more than twice as many as the blind." "Adverting to the fact that schools had been already established in this country and that Connecticut should not be behind in any needed humane work for its afflicted children," the committee, with the blessings of Governor William T. Minor, recommended the erection of a building which would cost $40,000, asking the Legislature for $25,000, the rest to come from "public benevolence." A bill to this effect (with the sum reduced to $15,000) passed the House of Representatives with but five dissenting votes but the appropriation was lost in the Senate by the vote of its president. Thereupon, in 1858, Knight gave up his practice and opened his home at Lakeville for the care, treatment, and education of mental defectives. He carried on the struggle for several years alone. After much effort and many rebuffs, public interest was aroused. In May, 1861, a law was passed giving aid and support to a "limited number of the state's sad and hopeless ones." Knight, whose place became the Connecticut School of Imbeciles, was appointed as its superintendent. In 1864, the school was removed to a new building at Lakeland. At the dedication exercises, congratulatory letters were received from three heads (Wilbur, Kerlin, Brown) of the five institutions then in operation in the United States. Kerlin introduced the rudiments of what was later to become occupational therapy, conducted a regular school, and advocated a cottage plan in preference to a large edifice. Knight continued his work until his death on January 22, 1880. The Lakeland institution existed until 1917; it was closed when the state opened the Mansfield Training School.

1866

Once Howe, Wilbur, Parrish, Kerlin, Doren, and Knight had made a beginning, other people in other states became active. Kentucky opened an institution in 1860, Illinois in 1865, Iowa in 1877, Indiana and Minnesota in 1879, Kansas in 1881, California in 1885, Nebraska in 1887, New Jersey and Maryland in 1888, Michigan in 1895, Montana in 1896.

In 1898, twenty-four public institutions were maintained by nineteen states, and one by the City of New York.

By 1917, all but four states were making some institutional provision. Altogether, 37,200 patients were cared for — 31,361 in State-sponsored, 3,043 in other publicly supported, and 2,816 in private institutions.

CANADA

1876

The first school, intended specifically for low-grade patients, was opened at Orillia in the Province of Ontario in 1876.

RELATIVE LATECOMERS

By 1880, France, Switzerland, Germany, Holland, the Scandinavian Countries, Austria, several of the United States, Canada, Finland, Latvia had made provisions for the institutional care of mental defectives. A few other areas were slower in following this trend but managed to join the movement before the end of the 19th Century.

BELGIUM

1892

Some Brothers of Charity opened in 1892 at Heinault an asylum for idiots and epileptics (270 children) who, divided into improvables, non-improvables, and cripples, received little beyond the most primitive care. Similar conditions existed at Tessenderloo (Limburg) which was started in 1895 with a capacity of 200. In the same year, some Sisters of Charity began to conduct a private institution at Heinault "in closer accord with modern ideas." At about the same time, a few other places were made available by brotherhoods and sisterhoods.

ITALY

1889

Professor Antonio Gonnelli-Cioni founded the first Italian school for mental defectives in 1889 at Chiavari, transferred later to Vercurago in the province of Bergamo. In six years, the number increased from fourteen to forty. There were classes in the 3 R's, drawing, music, and manual training.

1898

Dr. Sante de Sanctis, aided by some charitable women, started an asylum in Rome. In the same year, Bonfigli, the director of the psychiatric hospital, was instrumental in the creation of a national league for the protection of backward children. The Italian Minister of Education gave the following endorsement: "The aim of the league is in the highest degree worthy of a civilized country, since in seeking to bridge a hiatus in pedagogic methods, and to complete our series of educational institutions, it proposed to extend the benefits of education to feebleminded children and thus to protect society from the menace which the presence of so large a number of irresponsibles forming an element at once burdensome and dangerous cannot fail to present."

Tamburini, professor of psychiatry at the University of Bologna and head of a mental hospital, succeeded in having a "medico-pedagogic school," the institution of San Giovanni Persichete, inaugurated in 1899 with classrooms, workshops, a farm, a theater, music halls, a gymnasium, and a section of hydrotherapeutics.

JAPAN

R. Ishii, director of an orphanage, wrote this letter to Dr. Martin Barr:

1900

"In 1890, there took place in Nagoya, about 200 miles south of Toyko, a great earthquake, which destroyed about 10,000 lives. Naturally, there were left a number of helpless orphans. So I gathered some of those poor little ones and opened my orphanage. Among them was an imbecile child. This has caused me to open the department for the feebleminded children. Some more of the latter were added soon after, and there live with me six of them now. A new building is just going to be finished, and twenty more of the feebleminded are expected next month. There are nearly 200 applicants, but I have no room for any addition of inmates. My institution is a private one."

References

Almost all of the institutions named above issued either annual reports or occasional summaries of their activities. A considerable number of these statements, addressed to boards, legislatures, or the general public, are available in the U. S. National Medical Library, others are contained in the files of the individual institutions. They not only represent valuable source material but also reflect sentiments, appeals, and evolving trends. In addition to these, the following books, pamphlets, and articles offer an adequate account of the events during the "era of institutional expansion."

Barr, M. W.: *Mental Defectives*. Philadelphia, Blakiston. Chapter II: History, 1904, pp. 24-77.

Barthold, F.: *Der Idiotismus und seine Bekämpfung*. Stettin, Nahmer. 1868.

Brandes, G.: *Der Idiotismus und die Idioten-Anstalten mit besonderer*

Rücksicht auf die Verhältnisse im Königreich Hannover. Hannover, Rumpler. 1862.

Dahl, L.: *Bidrag til Kundskab on de Sindssyge i Norge.* Christiania, Steen. 1859.

Disselhoff, J.: *Die gegenwärtige Lage der Cretinen, Blödsinnigen und Idioten in den christlichen Ländern.* Bonn, Marcus. 1857.

Erlenmeyer, A. A.: *Übersicht der öffentlichen und privaten Irren- und Idioten-Anstalten aller europäischen Staaten.* Neuwied, Heuser. 1863.

——————: *Übersicht der Schweizerischen Irren- und Idiotenanstalten..* Neuwied, Heuser. 1877.

Fernald, W. E.: *History of the Treatment of the Feebleminded.* Boston, Geo. H. Ellis. 1912.

Ferrus, G. M. A.: Rapport au ministre de l'Intérieur sur l'établissement privé d'Edouard Séguin, rue Pigalle, No. 6, pour le traitement et l'éducation des enfants idiots, June 24, 1840. Reproduced in *Archives de Neurologie, 30:*264, 1895.

Haskell, R. H.: Mental Deficiency over a Hundred Years. A Brief Historical Sketch of Trends in This Field. *Am. J. Psychiat,* Centennial Anniversary Issue, 1944, pp. 107-118.

Hübertz, J. R.: *De Sindessyge i Denmark.* Kjöbenhavn, Möller. 1851.

Kerlin, I. N.: Notes on a Visit Among Several Foreign Institutions in 1889. Proceed. Asso. Med. Officers of Amer. Institutions for Idiotic and Feebleminded Children. 1891, pp. 39-41.

Kern, K. F.: *Pädagogisch-diätetische Behandlung Schwach- und Blödsinniger.* Leipzig, Klinkhardt. 1847.

Koetsvelt, C. E. von: *Het idiotisme en de Idioten-School.* Schoonhaven, van Nooten. 1856-7.

Kuhlmann, F.: One Hundred Years of Special Care and Training. *Am. J. Ment. Deficiency, 45:*8-24, 1940.

Laehr, H.: *Die Idioten-Anstalten Deutschlands und der benachbarten deutschen Länder.* Berlin, Reimer. 1874.

Müller, J.: Some observations of the Scotch and Danish Institutions for the Feeble-Minded. Proceed. Asso. Med. Officers Amer. Instit. Idiots and Feeblem. Persons, 1886, pp. 305-310.

——————: Establishments for the Instruction of Abnormal Children in the Scandinavian Countries. *Ibid.,* 1886, pp. 311-314.

Raymond, C. S.: Retrospect and Prospect in Mental Deficiency. *Am. J. Ment. Deficiency, 49:*5-18, 1944.

Rösch, K. H.: *Neue Untersuchungen uber den Cretinismus in Würt-temberg*. Erlangen, Encke. 1844.

Saegert, C. W.: *Über die Heilung des Blödsinns auf intellectuellem Wege*. Berlin, Schröders Buchhandlung: Heft I, 1845; Heft II, 1846.

Sarauw und Teisen: Sketch of Professor Johann Keller's Life and the Work of his Institutions. Proceed. Asso. Med. Officers Amer. Instit. Idiot. & Feeblem. Persons, 1892, pp. 163-172.

Semelaigne, R.: *Les pionniers de la psychiatrie Française avant et après Pinel*. Paris, Baillière et fils, Vol I, 1930; Vol II, 1932.

Sengelmann, H.: *Die Alsterdorfer Anstalten, ein Lebensbild*. Frankfurt a. Main, Johs. Alt. 1871.

————: *Idiotophilus*. Norden, Diedr. Soltau. 1885.

Shuttleworth, G. E., and Potts, W. A.: *Mentally Deficient Children, Their Treatment and Training*. Philadelphia, Blakiston. (First ed. 1895); Fifth Ed. 1922: Chapter I, Historical Retrospect.

Voisin, A. F.: *De l'idiotie chez les enfants*. Paris, Baillière. 1843.

Whitney, E. A.: Some Stalwarts of the Past. *J. Ment. Deficiency,* 57:345-360, 1953.

Wildenskov, H. O.: The Care of Mental Defectives in Denmark and the Keller Institutions for Mental Defectives, *Ibid.*, 53:138-144, 1948.

Wollen, W.: Mental Deficiency in Poland and U.S.S.R., *Ibid.*, 63:205-213, 1958.

Note

The *American Journal of Mental Deficiency* has published brief historical sketches about a number of American institutions:

Chapter 4

Early Mental Deficiency Periodicals

M ANY OF THE new institutions could come into existence only after church-sponsored or lay philanthropic organizations of an area had made the need known and got the necessary funds together. Sometimes special societies or ad hoc committees were formed with this as the avowed purpose. All of them were of a local character.

When the first establishments were opened, they had little contact with each other beyond occasional mutual visits by members of the staffs. With the spread of the movement, the time seemed ripe for some form of interchange of ideas and experiences.

BEOBACHTUNGEN ÜBER DEN CRETINISMUS

After Rösch had begun his work at Mariaberg in 1847, it occurred to him that the awakened interest in mental deficiency was scattered about in different places. He felt that there should be an instrument of communication as a common platform for all the people engaged in the study and care of the feebleminded. In 1850, he founded a journal, *Beobachtungen über den Cretinismus,* which, as far as can be ascertained, was the first periodical devoted exclusively to mental deficiency.

The first issue appeared in Tübingen, printed by H. Laupp. It was edited by the physicians of Mariaberg and financed from the budget of this institution. In the preface, dated November 1849, Rösch expressed the hope that the new journal would consititute a common organ for all pertinent contributions. The issue contained two lenghty articles: Rösch and his assistant, Dr. Krais, presented a report of the activities during the first two years of the existence of Mariaberg and appended twenty elaborate case histories. Friedrich Betz of Heilbronn wrote about his "physiologic-pathologic investigations of two cretin skulls." The second issue, printed in 1851, gives evidence of a wider

Beobachtungen

über den Cretinismus.

Eine Zeitschrift

herausgegeben von den

Aerzten der Heilanstalt Mariaberg.

Zum Besten und auf Kosten der Anstalt.

Inhalt des ersten Heftes.

1) Bericht der Heil- und Erziehungs-Anstalt Mariaberg während der ersten zwei Jahre ihres Bestehens; von dem Vorstande Dr. Rösch und dem Hausarzte Dr. Krais.

2) Physiologisch-pathologische Untersuchungen über Cretinen-Schädel; von Friedrich Betz in Tübingen.

Tübingen, 1850.

In Commission der H. Laupp'schen Buchhandlung.

scope. By that time Rösch was no longer director at Mariaberg. His interest and editorship of the journal continued, however. There was a new subtitle: "A journal in conjunction with several physicians and directors of institutions for feebleminded children."

Troxler, professor of philosophy at the University of Berne, contributed the lead article: *Rhapsodies about Cretinism, Idiotism, and Related Evils;* praising Guggenbühl and quoting extensively from Reil and from Esquirol, he made a strong point of the curability of these conditions. Erlenmeyer, producing statistical tables, wrote on microscopic-chemical examinations of the blood, feces, and urine of feebleminded children. Betz discussed the pathologic anatomy of cretinism. Rösch attempted to work out a differential diagnosis between insanity (*Verrücktheit*) in early life and cretinism (*mental deficiency*). The review of a book, *Das Leben der Cretinen,* by Jacob Heinrich Helferich and short notices about newly founded institutions conclude this issue. Mention is made of activities in Edinburg on behalf of mental defectives, the new centers in England (Bath and Highgate), and the efforts made in Massachusetts by Samuel Gridley Howe.

A third issue came out in 1852. Meyer-Ahrens of Zurich gave a historical review of the prevalence of cretinism in Switzerland prior to 1840. Friedrich Karl Stahl discussed the probable causes of cretinism in the valleys of Chamonnix and Aosta. Karl Zimmer (who succeeded Krais) offered a running account of the activities at Mariaberg. There were five book reports: Guggenbühl's *Sendschreiben* addressed to the British philanthropist, Lord Ashley; Rösch's treatise on institutions for mental defectives, with special consideration of those in Württemberg; Stahl's monograph on causes, nature, prognosis, and treatment of cretinism; Erlenmeyer's book on the curability of feebleminded children; Grange's study on the prevalence of goiter and cretinism in France.

There were notices on the progress of the existing centers and a report by Guggenbühl on his visit to what he called his foster children (institutions modeled after the Abendberg).

There was no further issue. Rösch, unhappy about the

political reaction which followed the 1848 upheavals, left Germany for the United States. Thus ended the first mental deficiency periodical.

ZEITSCHRIFT FUR DAS IDIOTENWESEN

In 1874, Pastor Sengelmann took it on himself to arrange for a conference of directors of the German institutions for mental defectives. The first meeting was held in Berlin on November 4-6 of the same year; the subsequent sessions took place in three-year intervals. Sengelmann was elected president for several consecutive terms. As is often the case on such occasions, the question of publicity came up. In 1881, the educators W. Schröter and E. Reichel started a new journal, *Zeitschrift für das Idiotenwesen,* which the conference of directors promptly adopted as its official organ.

The journal had an ambitious program. It was to include the following topics:

1. The concept, nature, and grouping of idiotism and the accompanying phenomena.

2. Its frequency, its causes, and the means for its cure and prevention.

3. Its treatment, educational measures in the home and in the institutions, principles and methods of instruction.

4. Planning and administration of institutions, return to society of those educated, their placement, support and supervision, and their civil and ecclesiastic rights.

5. Institutional and extramural statistics and their results.

6. Care of idiots in different countries.

7. Points of contact with allied areas, especially insanity and deafmutism.

In 1885, the title of the journal was changed to *Zeitschrift für die Behandlung Schwachsinniger and Epileptiker.* The new program was to include attention to childhood psychoses and convulsive disorders. The editorship was augmented by a physician, Dr. Wildermuth, who for years had reviewed the literature of "Idiocy and Cretinism" for *the Allgemeine Zeitschrift für Psychiatrie.*

Both the triennial conferences and the journal were dominated by theologians and educators. Of fifty-seven participants at the Stuttgart meeting in 1880, only eleven were medical men, and of these only four took an active part in the deliberations. Of the forty-six persons attending the 1883 conference in Hamburg, only eight were physicians.

The papers read at the conferences and those published in the journal reflect this professional distribution. Indeed, a contemporary reviewer of the Stuttgart meeting went out of his way to deplore what he regarded as lack of medical, especially psychiatric, interest. Much time was taken up by theological issues. Pastoral influences on the patients were declared to be more important than either medical or pedagogical services. Prayers for and by the inmates were declared to be the principal methods, and "strengthening of the Christian character" the principal aim. A big debate arose about whether feebleminded youngsters should be confirmed. It was urged that a ruling of the Evangelical Consistory of the Kingdom of Saxony be generally adopted. The ruling said: "Feebleminded children who have at least some knowledge of the three articles of the Christian faith may not be excluded from confirmation." This raised a weighty question: Should a confirmed idiot be allowed to swear an oath as a court witness? A compromise was reached which said that such a person may be called as a witness, but without administering the oath. Under no circumstances, however, should he, though duly confirmed, be drafted into military service.

Most of the non-theological discussions centered around the problems of education. Instruction in reading, gymnastic exercises (*Turnen*). and methods of punishment came in for detailed consideration.

A novel idea began to be voiced in those early volumes: Not all feebleminded children belong in institutions. There were reports of the first classes (in Dresden, in Elberfeld, and in Christiania [Oslo]) connected with regular schools. The practice found many critics, and there were many arguments about the pros and cons of such an innovation.

In 1929, the name of the journal was changed to *Zeitschrift für die Behandlumg Anormaler* (published by Marhold, Halle a.S.).

ZEITSCHRIFT FÜR DIE ERFORSCHUNG UND BEHANDLUNG
DES JUGENDLICHEN SCHWACHSINNS

H. Vogt of the University of Göttingen and W. Weygandt, then of the University of Würzburg, contracted in 1907 with the publishing firm of Gustav Fischer in Jena to publish a journal with the above title. Its program is contained in the rather lengthy subtitle: "Central organ for the overall scientific study, anatomy, clinical features, and pathology of juvenile feeble-mindedness and allied areas; for the care and treatment of the feebleminded; for education; for the organization of special schools and institutions; for the pertinent fields of criminology, forensic psychiatry, any psychology, with special consideration of the normal and abnormal mental development in childhood." In the foreword, the editors deplored the lack of a journal which dealt with the subject from a psychiatric point of view and emphasized the need for a multidisciplinary approach and the pulling together of the thitherto scattered efforts. There was a long list of famous people who promised contributions; among them were Freud, Bleuler, Alzheimer, Aschaffenburg, Bonhoeffer, von Monakow, Marburg, Czerny, Pfaundler, — certainly great leaders in psychiatry, neurology, and pediatrics, few of whom lived up to their promise.

Six issues (*Hefte*) appeared every year until the first World War. After a long pause, publication was resumed in 1922 but stopped altogether at the end of the year.

These volumes, especially the first seven, are a mine of important information. Volume I contained papers on speech development of retarded children (by the noted logopedist H. Gutzmann), psychological studies of stereognosis (by Clapa-rède), cerebral angiodystrophy, microcephaly, the historically significant article by Weygandt on idiocy and schizophrenia (pp. 311-332), military service, and occipital hydroencephal-ocele. Mention was made of the introduction of juvenile courts in the United States, Canada, Ireland, and Adelaide, Australia; Weygandt expressed the opinion that "in Germany an attempt would be difficult but by no means fruitless." (Two years later, in volume 3, there is a report of the first German juvenile court conference held in Charlottenburg on March 16-18, 1909.)

Volume 2 brought the classical paper by the Viennese educator T. Heller on dementia infantilis (known as Heller's disease). There were papers on tuberous sclerosis (H. Vogt), ophthalmologic findings in retarded children, cerebral changes in congenital syphilis, epilepsy in siblings, sexual education of the mentally retarded, and children's suicide.

An obituary by Weygandt in volume 3 gave an excellent biographic sketch of Bourneville (who was the first to describe tuberous sclerosis).

Among other outstanding contributions were H. Vogt's articles on "idiotia thymica" (volume 4) and Büttner's discussion of "word-blind" children (volume 7), one of the earliest papers on specific dyslexia.

After the first seven volumes with their wealth and variety of scientific contributions, the eighth and last volume is rather disappointing. There were no original studies. There were mostly reports of the activities of various institutions and of administrative matters. An interesting article discussed the influence in Germany of the work of Itard, Seguin, and Montessori.

The last paper of the last volume (pp. 278-289) was a sad farewell by Weygandt, who regretted the fact that the financial situation (at the height of the German inflation) had made it impossible for the publisher to continue the Journal.

PROCEEDINGS OF THE ASSOCIATION OF MEDICAL OFFICERS OF AMERICAN INSTITUTIONS FOR IDIOTIC AND FEEBLE-MINDED PERSONS

"The occasion of the Centennial Exhibition at Philadelphia in 1876, bringing together people of all classes, from all parts of our country, seemed to make it feasible for the first time to call an assemblage of representatives of institutions devoted to the care and education of idiots and feeble-minded children; accordingly, the management of the Pennsylvania Training School issued an invitation to all other existing institutions in the United States to meet at Media, Pennsylvania, which invitation was favorably responded to."

The group which met on June 6-8, consisted of I. N. Kerlin, who had extended the invitation, E. O. Seguin, of New York City; H. B. Wilbur, of Syracuse, N. Y.; G. A. Doren, of Columbus, Ohio.; C. T. Wilbur of Jacksonville, Ill.; H. M. Knight, of Lakeville, Conn.; and G. Brown, of Barre, Mass.

On June 7, the following Constitution was adopted "after various amendments":

Article I. The name of the Association shall be "The Association of Medical Officers of American Institutions for Idiots and Feeble-Minded Persons."

Article II. The object of the Association shall be the discussion of all questions relating to the causes, conditions, and statistics of idiocy, and to the management, training and education of idiots and feeble-minded persons; it will also lend its influence to the establishment and fostering of institutions for this purpose.

Article III. The members should be balloted in by a unanimous vote, and shall be composed of the medical heads of existing institutions, and of such persons who have distinguished themselves by their interest in this definite class.

Article IV. The officers shall consist of a President, Vice-President, Secretary and Treasurer, and an Executive Committee of three, who shall be elected annually, or in failure thereof, the officers in place shall continue to act.

Article V. The duties of the Executive Committee shall be to call special meetings; to make proper arrangements therefor; if desirable, to assign to members subjects for special reports; to take charge of arrangements for the publication of all proceedings referred, and to perform such other duties as may be required.

Article VI. The regular meetings shall be held annually, at a time and place to be designated by the association.

Seguin was elected president, H. B. Wilbur vice-president, Kerlin secretary and treasurer. The executive committee consisted of H. B. Wilbur, Seguin, and Kerlin.

Seven additional persons were elected to membership: Blackie of Nashville, Ayres of Fort Wayne, Doren of Columbus, Mrs. Dr. Brown of Barre, E. O. Seguin of New York. Provisions were made for honorary membership for "trustees or managers of the institutions."

The participants at the first meeting of the newly formed Association on June 7, 1876, passed the following resolution: "That the Executive Committee make arrangements with some medico-psychological journal to act as the organ of the Association in publication of its proceedings." The Chicago Journal of Mental Science was suggested; negotiations to this effect apparently did not work out satisfactorily. At the second meeting in Columbus, Ohio, Dr. Kerlin moved "that the Executive Committee be authorized to publish such parts of the minutes and papers of this and of last year's proceedings as they may deem proper in the form of pamphlet transactions." The motion was carried by unanimous vote.

The first issue contained accounts of the first two meetings and the constitution of the organization. Four papers read before the assembly were printed:

Monograph of G.C.P., by Edward Seguin. ("A typical case of sensorial idiocy.")

The Organization of Establishments for the Idiots and Imbecile Classes, by Isaac Kerlin. ("Some of the principles which are believed to underlie the whole subject of the care, training, and grouping into homes and schools for the interesting persons who claim our sympathies, and to whom our lives are devoted.")

Prevention of Mental Disease, by Mrs. C. W. Brown (A pious, logically written appeal to consideration of both body and soul.)

The Classification of Idiocy, by H. B. Wilbur. (Largely a presentation of Ireland's grouping.)

The proceedings were published annually. In September, 1896, the rather cumbersome title was changed to *Journal of Psycho-Asthenics,* "devoted to the care, training and treatment of the feeble-minded and epileptics." The new name was explained in an editorial:

"Inasmuch as the term Psycho-Asthenics is not found in any dictionaries, its appearance as a new word justly calls for an explanation — if not for an apology. This must be found in the fact that there is no universal, or even very general use that implies a knowledge of that condition which is termed idiocy or feeble-mindedness; and even in the use of these terms as applied to conditions, custom varies as to which is generic and which specific. By bringing into use well-known fixed roots that indicate by their form and arrangement the use intended, accurate expression at least will be realized so far as the term is approved and adopted."

The journal was published quarterly at Faribault, Minn., with A. C. Rogers as editor. It ceased publication in 1918. The Association then resumed the annual Proceedings until 1937.

In 1906, at the 30th annual session, the Association itself changed its name to American Association for the Study of the Feebleminded and again in 1933 to American Association on Mental Deficiency (AAMD) and became incorporated on March 11, 1938 in the Court of Common Pleas of Delaware County, Pennsylvania. In 1940, the name of the Journal was changed to *American Journal of Mental Deficiency* to be published quarterly. The first issue appeared as Volume XLV in 1940-1941 under the editorship of Edward J. Humphreys. The editorial announcing the change of name reads as follows:

"The American Association on Mental Deficiency over a period of sixty-four years has endeavored to inform lay and scientific groups of the annual progress of the work of the Association and its members. The medium of information during the earlier years was the *Journal of Psycho-Asthenics* which became the Proceedings of the Association. A growing feeling that the work of the Association would be considerably advanced by the publication of a quarterly journal has led to the establishment of The American Journal of Mental Deficiency, of which this is the first number . . . In view of the colossal social revolution through which the world is passing, what justification is there for the expenditure of time, human energy and money on a publication interested primarily in mental defective and subcultural individuals? If our attention to the problems of the mentally defective and the subcultural groups is centered around custodianship alone, there is hardly any justification for such a journal. If, however, we conceive our field in the broader terms of arrest in human development, we face the need to discover why such arrests occur, how they affect human society and what may be done to diminish these deficiencies in human stock and in social organization. The justification of the Journal then becomes self-evident.

"The study of human deficiencies extends far beyond the province of any one professional group, or state or community organization. The field of developmental deficiency in its broadest sense leads us to consider man in the psychobiological terms of the organism functioning as a unit in relation to physical, intellectual, conational, affective-emotional, temperamental and characterial integrations. No single field of the medical or social sciences can become the 'be-all and end-all' in the study of human development; it is necessary to include all fields and workers — administrational, clinical, educational and research. In recognition of the varied aspects of our work, the Journal in each issue will include the following divisions: genetics; auxology (chemistry, physiology, physical anthropology); neurology; psychology; psychiatry; education, sociology; eugenics, and other topics. The complexity of the divisions represented, and their inter-relationships, requires the utmost in democratic organization of both the Journal and the field as-a-whole.

"It may finally be said, that by challenging our intellectual powers these scientific and social problems in the field of mental defect may assist us in the recognition of the nature of human deficiency and of the need for healthy development in the emotional-social life of all mankind."

Note

Milligan, G. E.: History of the American Association on Mental Deficiency, *Am. J. Ment. Defic.*, 66: 357-369, 1961, contains a concise account of the development of the AAMD. It has the following subtitles: Origin; Purposes, Growth of Knowledge; Nature of Mental Deficiency; Public School Special Classes; Name Changed and Objectives expanded; Persons Who Have Served the Association with Distinction; Growth of Institutions; Membership and Organization; Publications; Research.

Chapter 5

Shifting Goals of Institutional Care

W HEN THE FIRST attempts were made to care for mental defectives in residential settings, the unbounded zeal of the young innovators envisioned a "cure," an attainment of "normalcy," as a result of their efforts. Such was the firm conviction of Guggenbühl and the pious hope of Seguin, Rösch, Saegert, and others. Educative, "physiological," "moral," and some medical measures were expected to improve intelligence through exercise of the mental functions. As late as 1877, Seguin referred to the "common observation" that the effects of educating the brain show themselves in a noticeable enlargement of the cranium.

When Itard did not succeed in civilizing Victor of Aveyron, when the inmates of the Abendberg failed to live up to Guggenbühl's expectations and promises, when the children in the newly-founded institutions did not make the anticipated gains after years of residence, the original notion of "curability" underwent considerable weakening. It is true that some of the pioneers, not less enthusiastic than the others, had been more realistic from the start. Amelioration, rather than normalcy, was the goal set by Howe who, in his report to the legislature of Massachusetts, formulated the function of the planned institution as follows: "It would be demonstrated that no idiot need be confined or restrained by force; that the young can be trained to industry, order and self-respect; that they can be redeemed from

83

odious and filthy habits; and that there is not one of any age who may not be made more of a man, and less of a brute, by patience and kindness, directed by energy and skill." Indeed, Seguin himself recognized at an early time that some of the patients were impervious to education and expressed the fear that, with a preponderance of such cases, the institutions might become nothing more than "asylums for the incurable."

This danger did not seem to exist at the outset when each new venture started with a small number of pupils and every child could be made the center of an all-out effort more or less in emulation of the work done and advocated by Itard and Seguin. But it did not take long for the admissions to multiply. Many of the places, when they opened their doors, took in fewer than a dozen and hardly any had more than a score. The situation changed radically in the course of two decades. Occupancies in the 1870's ran into the hundreds and there were waiting lists. By that time it had become clear that, contrary to the initial optimism, a considerable portion of the institutional population was there to stay indefinitely, with no prospect of being returned to their communities. This realization led to a modification of the previously anticipated objective. The institution was viewed as a lifetime home for many of the inmates, who therefore had better be trained for permanent retention and taught to give service in the confines of the school. "Physiological" training was superseded by occupational training. As Kuhlmann put it in an apt historical review: "Skill became a substitute for intelligence."

Even for those who might eventually be sent back to their homes, the mere instruction in the three R's was found to be an inadequate preparation. The concept of a "school" was widened to include the acquisition of useful skills in various occupations. This idea resulted in the installation of shops for industrial training.

Thus the institution was bound to lose its initial unitary character. A few European centers, prominently the one established by Johann Keller in Denmark and taken over by his son, began at an early date (in the 1850's) to accommodate defectives of different degrees of severity in several subdivisions: a "school proper," an "industrial section," and an "asylum." In the United States, a similar development took place in the 1870's. Kuhlmann described the conditions existing by 1875 thus:

"There are now twenty-five State Schools, almost universally spoken of as institutions . . . The inmates number something over 15,000. The institution now usually includes an administration building or wing, a school plant with class rooms and training equipment, separate dormitories arranged for inmates, classified according to age, sex, and grade of mental deficiency, or physical condition. It has shops for industrial training and land for farming and dairying. It has its own power, light, and heating plant, kitchen, bakery, and laundry, as well as hospital where at times attendants and nurses receive special training for their duties in the institution. In its major physical aspects the institution has already become of age. Abandonment of the idea of cure was the important factor in the development of the physical plant."

It is well to remember that the pioneering founders and supporters of institutions were motivated by the desire, often inspired by religious ardor, to serve the needs of the individual mental defective. Imperceptibly at first, but then more and more conspicuously, the public and professional emphasis shifted away from the patients themselves toward a consideration of the needs of society, which was to be protected from the harm done by their presence in the community. A feeling that society was in serious danger created an atmosphere of growing alarm. The mental defectives were viewed as a menace to civilization, incorrigible at home, burdens to the school, sexually promiscuous, breeders of feebleminded offspring, victims and spreaders of poverty, degeneracy, crime, and disease. Consequently, there was a cry for the segregation of all mental defectives, with the aim of purifying society, of erecting a solid wall between it and its contaminators. According to Kuhlmann, "the view that all mental defectives should be committed to state institutions for life grew rapidly after the momentum it had gained by 1900. In another ten years, it had become unanimous as opinion ever had been on anything concerning mental defectives. The question was apparently settled."

This social indictment was reinforced by the publication of scaring surveys by scared surveyors (a brief anthology of which has been offered by Davies). Wallin, in retrospect, summed up the "multiple indictments" as follows:

1. The mentally deficient are prolific.

2. Their progeny, illegitimate as well as legitimate, are mentally deficient, neuropathic, or dysgenic.

3. This group has strong criminalistic propensities.

4. They are a prime source of sex irregularities, promiscuity, prostitution, and perversion.

5. There is a close association between mental defectiveness and alcoholism with respect to genesis and consequences.

6. Occupational incompetence, destitution, pauperism, and vagrancy are frequent among this group.

Institutions had been begun in the mid-19th Century with the idea that they were to benefit mentally defective children, who until then had been neglected by society. Fifty years later, when such places had been accepted features of many civilized commonwealths, we find them viewed as areas of detention of undesirable elements for the benefit of society. The pleas for their maintenance and enlargement carried tunes altogether different from the hymns of hope intoned by the originators of the notion of institutional care and training as constructive, therapeutic enterprises.

References

Davies, S. P., and Ecob, K. Q.: *The Mentally Retarded in Society.* New York, Columbia University Press. 1959.

Kuhlmann, F.: One Hundred Years of Special Care and Training. *American Journal of Mental Deficiency, 45*:8-24, 1940.

Seguin, E. O.: Monograph of G. C. P. A Typical Case of Sensorial Idiocy. Proceed. Asso. Med. Officers Amer. Institutions for Idiotic and Feeble-Minded Persons, 1877, p. 11-18.

Wallin, J. E. W.: *Education of Mentally Handicapped Children.* New York, Harper & Bros., 1955, p. 417.

Chapter 6

From Homogeneity to Heterogeneity

Until about the middle of the nineteenth century, "idiocy" was thought of as a more or less unitary condition. The relatively few passages in compendia and the still fewer monographs dealt with idiocy, amentia, fatuitas, imbecillitas, stupiditas, stultitia, or morosis as a homogeneous characteristic. As late as in 1824, Belhomme declared categorically that cretins "present the only variety which can be found in idiocy," adding that some people were in the habit of getting albinos mixed up with idiots; he cited several examples of intelligent albinos to show this to be in error. Some, indeed, conceived of cretinism as the unifying feature and, following Troxler, subdivided it into four distinctive forms: endemic goiter, albinism, deafmutism, and idiocy. (The connection between cretinism and deafmutism was based on the widespread notion that the thyroid was a part of the vocal apparatus.)

While most authors recognized cretinism as a special variety, reference to its specificity does not seem to have precluded the use of this designation indiscriminately for all mental defectives. Hence we find the terms cretinism and idiocy often used interchangeably in the early literature. Guggenbühl took into the Abendberg all kinds of defectives even though he claimed that his institution was solely one for cretins. He announced that "we may consider as mentally weak, and therefore, on the road to cretinism, *all* children who neither at home nor in school can be made accessible to the ordinary means of education and instruction." Rösch's publications, which discussed idiocy in the broadest sense of the word, were invariably captioned as treatises or observations on "cretinism." Griesinger, who was closely associated with Rösch as one of the directors at Mariaberg, found it necessary to halt this trend and to declare emphatically: "Every cretin is an idiot, but every idiot is not a cretin; idiocy is the more comprehensive term, cretinism is a special kind of it."

ENDEMIC CRETINISM

Probably the earliest mention of endemic goiter was made by (Decimus Junius) Juvenal (ca. 60-140 A.D.), who wrote in the 13th satire, verse 162: *Quis tumidum guttur miratur in Alpibus?*, and by Marcus Vitruvius Pollio (1st Century A.D.), the voyaging architect, who found swollen goiters (guttura) in Northern Italy and in the Alpine regions (*Guttur homini tumescit praesertim apud agricolas Italiae et Medullos Alpinos*), suggesting the nature of the drinking water as a possible cause (I, 8, c. 3).

For centuries, the apathetic and stolid appearance of the dwarfed cretins, with their puffed eyelids, baggy cheeks, depressed noses, and large protruded tongues, had been an object of superstitious preoccupation. The condition was endemic in several areas of the globe, especially the Andes of South America, the Himalayas of Asia, and the Pyrenees and Alpine valleys of Europe. Mention began to be made of it in the accounts of travelers in Switzerland, Austria, and France since the beginning of the 16th Century. In 1507, Wellendorfer reported seeing *strumosos homines* of both sexes in Salzburg whither they had migrated from Carinthia. Stumpf, in 1586, told of their prevalence around the Swiss village of Trimmis. Diego Velasquez (1599-1662), who painted several "fools" of King Philip IV of Spain (the dwarfs El Primo and Antonio el Ingles and the idiots El Bobo di Coria and Don Sebastian de Morra), left in one of his masterpieces, El Niño de Valleca, the portrait of what probably was a typical cretin.

Diego Rodriguez de Silva y Velasquez (1599-1660), El Niño de Vallecas, Prado Museum, Madrid.

The etymology of the word cretin is uncertain. Fodéré believed that it was a corruption of *chrétien*, or Christian, because due to their simplicity of mind people so afflicted were incapable of sinning. Indeed, a number of authors (Core, 1781; Bourrit,

1782) reported that in some Swiss villages they were venerated as saintly persons. On the other hand, Iphofen (1804) thought that the root was *cretira,* a form of *creature,* "un benêt (a simpleton), une bonne créature." Others, e.g., Rösch, saw the origin in *creta* (chalk), because of the grayish-white, pasty, "chalky" color of the skin, analogous to the term *Kreidling* used in some regions of Germany. Conversely, the inhabitants of the valley of Aosta referred to cretins as *marrons* because of their dark, "chestnut-colored" complexion.

Esquirol made this suggestion: "May I be permitted to venture a hypothesis as to the origin of this expression? Might not the term cretin come from the obsolete word *cretine* which has the same meaning as alluvium? Has not this name been transfered to individuals who have become infirm in consequence of having dwelt upon an alluvial soil? In fact, is not cretinism endemic in such mountain gorges as are very swampy and exposed to damp air?"

It is rather difficult to be sure about the nature of a group of people in Southern France, called *cagots* in Gascogne, *caffots* in Navarre, and *gahets, gabets,* or *caffets* in Guyenne, who were said to be Pyrenean or Basque "tribes afflicted with cretinism." According to Michel (1847) and de Rochas (1876), they were "a sort of parias, analogous to those of India, for whom prejudices and customs prohibited any contact with their compatriots. They lived in separate quarters at some distance from the villages. They wore on their garments a distinctive badge so that people would know to keep away from them. They were under the jurisdiction of the Church, which was a stern master." Different theories about their origin were propounded: 1) They were said to be remnants of the Visigoths who had been defeated by Clovis I in 507 in the plains of Vouillé; 2) They were Arabs or Saracens left behind after their armies had been repulsed by Charles Martel in 732; 3) They were Goths driven out of Spain; 4) They were afflicted with "an attenuated form of leprosy." While the terms *cagots* and *cretins* have sometimes been used synonymously, it is highly improbable that all members of these communities, continuing for generations and, wherever permitted to do so, working proficiently as cobblers, basket makers, and carpenters, having good communication among each other, and taking care of themselves and their offspring, were nothing but cretins. Indeed, Auzouy gave in 1867 a moving account of the life of the cagots, whom he considered "so altogether different from cretins" that they have scarcely any claim to the special attention of the medical profession." He thought that the name derives from Ca(nis) Got(hus), *chien de Goth,* a token of the contempt in which they were held by the rest of the population. He was certain that, if given access to the cultural life of their contemporaries, they would make good citizens.

It was Felix Plater (1536-1614) who first spoke of endemic cretinism as congenital feeblemindedness, or *stultitia originalis.* Credit, however, must be given to Paracelsus for having first noticed the coincidence between cretinism and mental deficiency and having called attention to this while he was professor of physic and surgery at the University of Basel (1526-1528) and later while in Salzburg; while goiter is not necessary characteristic of idiocy, he declared, yet it is most commonly found among them.

Plater's description (*capite infermi, interdum lingua immensa et tumida, muti, strumoso simul aliquando gutture, aspectu deformi*) established reasonably definite diagnostic criteria. Similar characterizations came from the Dutch physician, Peter von Foreest (1522-1597) and the Swiss historian Josias Simler (in 1574). The Viennese court physician, Wolfgand Hoefer, in Hercules medicus (editions of 1657 and 1675), gave an equally clear account when he referred to the *multi strumosi et stulti* in Valesia (Wallis) and in the Austrian Alps.

It was not until the second half of the eighteenth century that major interest was aroused in scientific and governmental circles. Few publications, however, attracted as much attention as did the treatise, *Traité du goître et du crétinisme,* published in Turin in 1792 by Francois Emmanuel Fodéré.

Fodéré, born January 8, 1764, in Savoy, obtained his medical degree in 1787. There is a story (related by Semelaigne) that he got into trouble when, as a student, he had a body of a cretin exhumed to do an autopsy and to look for cerebral lesions. He had to leave his home, went for three years to Paris, then to London, and finally returned to Savoy, where he enlisted in the army. His treatise on cretinism made so great an impression that King Victor Amédée III of Savoy gave him a generous pension to travel and gather more information. As professor of experimental physics and chemistry, he published in 1799 a book on legal medicine and public health. He then was associated with the mental hospital in Marseille and, in 1814, accepted the chair of forensic medicine at the University of Strassburg. All of his biographers mention that his wife was a cousin of the wives of King Bernadotte of Sweden and of King Joseph Bonaparte of Spain and add that he never used this relationship to gain favors. He died February 4, 1835.

Fodéré, besides giving detailed descriptions of the "two diseases," goiter and cretinism, as afflictions of inhabitants of valleys, saw the cause in the saturation of stagnant air with moisture. He considered "the physical and moral measures" to be employed in order to prevent their occurrence in the future. The prophylactic suggestions were, of course, tailored to his ideas about etiology.

The medical concern, which threw itself almost suddenly on the subject of cretinism, is reflected in the literature. Even if one tries to the extent possible to set aside those writings which make no distinction between it and mental deficiency in general, the swelling tide of monographs kept mounting since the days of Fodéré, having started slowly a decade or two earlier, when Albrecht von Haller made known in 1772 his studies of the cretins in the canton of Waat (Waadt), Malacarne reported in 1788 on three autopsies, and Ackermann gave in 1790 a detailed description of cretin skulls.

Saint-Lager has compiled an exhaustive review of the opinions on etiology held by all authors who had ever written on cretinism before 1867. The chemical composition of drinking water leads in regard to frequency. Horace Benoit de Saussure of Geneva conceived the idea of the possible influence of geological formation on the water supply. Next come inadequacies of the air — cold and dry; moist; stagnant; insufficiently oxygenated; overloaded with sulfurous vapors; marshy or specific miasma; exposure of the neck to draught; vicissitudes of temperature. Dietary faults were accused by others — certain salts used in cooking; saltless food; cold water drunk while sweating; exclusive consumption of vegetables and milk; greasy food; parental drunkenness during procreation. Other recorded causes were lack of sunlight; lack of electricity; "exertion accompanied by tight clothes around the neck"; waywardness; masturbation; inbreeding. Some thought of the existence of multiple causes which, in addition to any of those enumerated above, include "absence of civilization" and "racial causes" (in the case of the *cagots*). Finally, a number of authors are quoted who confess: "*On ne sait rien.*"

In 1811, Napoleon Bonaparte, probably influenced by the impact of Fodéré's thesis, ordered a census of cretins to be taken in the canton of Wallis, then in the Department of Simplon, which showed the number there amounting to three thousand. He wanted the families to be transplanted to higher altitudes from the valleys in which the disease was prevalent. Nothing came of this, partly because the people refused to leave their homes and partly because Napoleon's power came to an end not long afterwards. There was, furthermore, a superstition among the villagers that the cretins in their midst were a sort of target of God's wrath which spared the rest of the populace; take them away and the ire of the Lord might look for other victims.

In the 1840's considerable activity began along two lines: statistical surveys and attempts to find a road to treatment.

On August 19, 1845, King Charles Albert of Sardinia, in a letter to the Chef du Magistrat du Protomédicat at Turin, called together a commission consisting of physicians, chemists, and geologists, to ascertain the number of cretins in his realm, visit the affected regions, and examine the soil in the different provinces of the kingdom. The report of this commission (Turin, Imprimérie royale, 1848) contains in its 224 pages a wealth of information about the prevailing notions regarding the affliction.

Johann Heinrich Zschokke (1771-1848), known in the history

of literature as one of the first writers of short stories, emigrated from his German home town of Magdeburg to the Swiss town of Graubünden, where he obtained a position in an educational institution. He urged the organization of a statistical study which was begun under his guidance and was completed in 1855, seven years after his death.

Surveys made in the following decade or two were not altogether reliable because of the notion of the homogeneity of all mental defectives and the resulting use of cretinism and idiocy as synonyms.

As for therapautic efforts, the first practical steps were taken by Guggenbühl. They were, of course, adapted to current concepts about etiology, with emphasis on high elevation away from the valleys, dietary regime, and more or less random medicinal experimentation. In the following decades, a number of theories vied with each other. Champault summed them up as doctrines of miasmatic intoxication, hydrotelluric origin, parasitic or microbic infection, multiple causation, and finally the assumption of iodine insufficiency.

It is the last of the theories that gained more and more ground. In 1855, Köstl proposed the therapeutic and prophylactic use of iodized salt in Austria. In 1859, Lombroso recommended that, as a means of preventing cretinism, all goitrous persons of marriageable age should be treated with iodine. Under the influence of Wagner von Jauregg, iodized salt was distributed in the total population of some of the affected regions in Central Europe.

Moritz Schiff (1823-1896) attempted, with little success, to cure cretinism by transplanting the entire thyroid gland from an animal. Experiments by Horsley (1857-1916), F. Howitz (1828-1912), H. Mackenzie (1856-1929), most of which were reported in the 1890's, led to the subcutaneous injection of thyroid juice, with somewhat better results. Subsequently, this was substituted by the dry extract given in tabloid form.

As time went on, clear distinction could be made between the different types of hypothyroidism. A committee of the Clinical Society of London summed up its conclusions as follows:

"There is strong evidence that myxedema, sporadic cretinism, endemic cretinism, cachexia strumipriva, and the operative myxedema of animals are species of one genus, and that the one pathological fact common to all these conditions is the occurrence of morbid processes involving destruction of the thyroid gland."

References

Abercrombie, J.: *De fatuitate Alpina.* Edinburgh, A. Neill. 1803.

Ackermann, J. F.: *Über die Kretinen, eine besondere Menschenabart in den Alpen. Gotha,* Ettinger. 1790.

Auzouy, M.: Les Crétins et les cagot des Pyreneés. *Annales médicopsychol.,* 1867, 4th series, Vol. 9, 1-31.

Blumenbach, J. F.: *In cretinismo capitis formatio singularis.* 1783.

Bourrit, M. T.: Desxription des Alpes Apennines et Rhétiennes. Genève. 1781 (German translation, Zürich, 1782, pp. 88; 95).

Champault, J.: Les conceptions sur le goître et le crétinisme de 1850 à 1910. Thèse de Paris, Les Presses Modernes. 1935.

Core, W.: Briefe über die natürlichen, bürgerlichen and politischen Zustände in der Schweiz. Zürich, 1781.

Cranefield, P. C.: The Discovery of Cretinism. *Bull. History Med.,* 36:489-511, 1962.

De Rochas, V.: *Les Parias de France et d'Espagne.* Paris. 1876.

Ferrus, G. M. A.: *Traité du goître et du crétinisme* Paris, 1851.

Fodéré, F. E.: *Traité du goître et du cretinisme.* Turin. 1791; Paris, Bernard, 1800.

Griesinger, W.: *Die Pathologie und Therapie der psychischen Krankheiten.* 4th ed. Braunschweig, Vieweg. 1876, p. 353.

Haller, A.: *Über Cretinen im Canton Waat. Bern,* Sammlung kleiner Hallerschen Schriften. 1772, p. 188.

Hoefer, W.: *Hercules medicus.* Vienna, Kürner, 1657, pp. 37-39.

Horsfield, E.: Mental Defectives at the Court of Philip IV of Spain as portrayed by the Great Court Painter Velasquez. *Am. J. Ment. Deficiency,* 45:152-157, 1940.

Iason, A. H.: *The Thyroid Gland in Medical History.* New York, Froben Press. 1946.

Iphofen, A. E.: *De Cretinismo.* Vitebergae, Graessler. 1804.

—————: *Der Cretinismus.* Dresden, Arnold. 1817.

Juvenal: Satire 13, line 162.

Köstl, F.: Der endemische Cretinismus als Gegenstand der öffentlichen Fürsorge. Denkschrift an seine Excellenz den Herrn Minister des Innern Dr. Alexander Freiherr von Bach. Wien, K. K. Hofdruckerei. 1855.

Lombroso, C.: Sulla microcephalia e sul cretinismo. Rivista Clinica di Bologna, 1873, fasc. 7, July.

Maffei, C.: De fexismo specie cretinismi. Landeshuti, Thomann. 1813.

Malacarne, M. V.: Lettre au Prof. Frank sur l'état des crétins de Turin au mois de Décembre 1788. In Frank, J. P. Delectus, opusc. med. Ticini, 4:241-258, 1789.

Merke, F.: The History of Endemic Goiter and Cretinism in the Thirteenth to Fifteenth Centuries. Proc. Royal Soc. Med., 53:995-1002, 1960.

Michel, F. X.: Histoire des races maudites de la France et de l'Espagne. Paris, A. Franck. 1847.

Nièpce, B.: Traité du goître et du cretinisme. Paris, Baillière, 1851.

Paracelsus: De generatione stultorum. Opera omnia. Liber Theophrasti, Tractatus I, 1603.

Platerus, F.: Praxeos medicae, etc. tractatus. Basel, Waldkirch. 1602, Vol I, 95.

—————: Observationum in hominis affectibus plerisque. Basel, König. 1614, p. 38.

Rapport de la commission créée par le roi de Sardigne pour étudier le crétinisme. Turin, Imprimérie royale. 1848.

Saint-Lager, J.: Études sur les causes du crétinisme et du goître endémique. Paris, Baillière & fils. 1867.

Saussure, H. B. de: Voyages dans les Alpes. Vol. I, Neufchatel, Fauche. 1786, Vol II, 480-495.

Simler, J.: Vallesiae descriptio, libri duo. Tiguri, Froschour. 1574. Reprinted in J. C. Fuessli, Thesaurus historiae Helveticae, Tiguri, Orellii. 1735, p. 8.

Stumpf, J.: Gemeiner Lobl. Eydgnoschaft Stetten, Landen und Völckern Chronickwidriger thaaten Beschreybung. Zurych, Froschour, 1548, vol. 2, fol. 319 b.

Troxler, I. P. V.: Der Cretinismus und seine Formen als endemische Menschenentartung in der Schweiz. Zürich. 1836.

Vitruvius: De architectura. Book 8, chapter 3, paragraph 20.

Wellendorffer: Decalogium Virgilii Salzburgensis de metheorologicis impressionibus et mirabilibus naturae operibus, Lipsiae, Stockel. 1507. Chap. VI, Fol. XLIV a.

Zschokke, T.: Über den Cretinismus im Bezirk Aarau. Annalen

Staatsarzneikunde von Schneider, Schurmayer und Hargt. 1840, Vol. 5, drittes Heft.

MONGOLISM

John Langdown Haydon Down (1828-1896), Physician to the Asylum for Idiots at Earlswood and Assistant Physician to, and Lecturer on Materia Medica at, the London Hospital, presented the following "clinical lecture and report" in 1866:

"I had for some time had my attention directed to the possibility of making a classification of the feeble-minded, by arranging them around various ethnic standards — in other words, framing a natural system to supplement the information to be derived by an inquiry into the history of the case.

"I have been able to find among the large number of idiots and imbeciles which come under my observation, both at Earlswood and the out-patient department of the hospital, that a considerable portion can be fairly referred to one of the great divisions of the human family other than the class from which they sprung. Of course, there are numerous representations of the great Caucasian family. Several well-marked examples of the Ethiopian variety have come under my notice, presenting the characteristic malar bones, the prominent eyes, the puffy lips, and retreating chin. The woolly hair has also been present, although not always black, nor has the skin acquired pigmentary deposit. They have been specimens of white negroes, although of European descent.

"Some arrange themselves around the Malay variety, and present in their soft, black, curling hair, their prominent upper jaws and capacious mouth, types of the family which people the South Sea Islands. Nor have there been wanting the analogues of the people who, with shortened foreheads, prominent cheeks, deep-set eyes, and slightly apish nose, originally inhabited the American Continent.

"The great Mongolian family has numerous representatives, and it is to this division I wish, in this paper, to call special attention. A very large number of congenital idiots are typical Mongols. So marked is this, that when placed side by side, it is difficult to believe that the specimens compared are not children of the same parents.

"The number of idiots who arrange themselves around the Mongolian type is so great, and they present such a close resemblance to one another in mental power, that I shall describe an idiot member of this racial division, selected from the large number that have fallen under my observation: —

"The hair is not black, as in the real Mongol, but of a brownish colour, straight and scanty. The face is flat and broad, and destitute of prominence. The cheeks are roundish, and extended laterally. The eyes are obliquely placed, and the internal canthi more than normally distant from one another. The palpebral fissure is very narrow. The forehead is wrinkled transversely, from the constant assistance which the levatores palpebrarum derive from the occipito-frontalis muscle in the opening of the eyes. The lips are large and thick, with transverse fissures. The tongue is long, thick, and is much roughened. The nose is small. The skin has a slight dirty-yellowish tinge, and is deficient in elasticity, giving the appearance of being too large for the body.

"The boy's aspect is such, that it is difficult to realise that he is the child of Europeans; but so frequently are these characters presented, that there can be no doubt that these ethnic features are the result of degeneration.

"The Mongolian type of idiocy occurs in more than 10 per cent of the cases which are presented to me. They are always congenital idiots, and never result from accidents after uterine life. They are, for the most part, instances of degeneracy arising from tuberculosis in the parents. They are cases which very much repay judicious treatment. They require highly azotized food, with a considerable amount of oleagenous material. They have considerable power of imitation, even bordering on being mimics. They are humorous, and a lively sense of the ridiculous often colours their mimicry. This faculty of imitation may be cultivated to a very great extent, and a practical direction given to the results obtained. They are usually able to speak; the speech is thick and indistinct, but may be improved very greatly by a well-directed scheme of tongue gymnastics. The co-ordinating faculty is abnormal, but not so defective that it cannot be greatly strengthened. By systematic training, considerable manipulative power may be obtained.

"The circulation is feeble; and whatever advance is made intellectually in the summer, some amount of retrogression may be expected in the winter. Their mental and physical capabilities are, in fact, directly as the temperature.

"The improvement which training effects in them is greatly in excess of what would be predicated if one did not know the characteristics of the type. The life expectancy, however, is far below the average, and the tendency is to the tuberculosis which I believe to be the hereditary origin of the degeneracy.

"Apart from the practical bearing of this attempt at an ethnic classification, considerable philosophical interest attaches to it. The tendency in the present day is to reject the opinion that the various races are merely varieties of the human family having a common origin, and to insist that climatic or other influences are sufficient to account for the different types of man. Here, however, we have examples of retrogression, or at all events, of departure from one type and the assumption of the characteristics of another.

"If these great racial divisions are fixed and definite, how come it that disease is able to break down the barrier, and so simulate so closely the features of the members of another division? I cannot but think that the observations which I have recorded are indications that the differences in the races are not specific, but variable.

"These examples of the result of degeneracy among mankind appear to me to furnish some arguments in favour of the unity of the human species."

There was no immediate reaction to Down's report. Independently of his work, Fraser presented on December 14, 1875, at Edinburgh a forty year old woman with "Kalmuc idiocy" (named after a Mongolian tribe), giving a detailed description of the symptoms. His demonstration was followed by Mitchell's account of sixty-two patients with the same features. Ireland, who was present at the meeting, said facetiously that he did not think that there were any Kalmucs in the East of Scotland and that one should exclude this patronymic from the kingdom of Fife. (Here the transcript records: *Laughter!*) Chairman Jamieson regarded the term "very objectionable" and declared that there was "no reason for nicknaming an idiot by calling him a Kalmuc."

As is sometimes the case with new discoveries, retrospect shows that similar observations were made by others around the time when Down, Fraser and Mitchell made their reports. Seguin described in 1866 as "furfuraceous cretinism" a syndrome possibly mongoloid. In 1873, Lombroso referred to the "mongolian atavism of the cretinoid anomaly."

It was Ireland who in 1877 made mongolism known to a wider public by including it in his *Idiocy and Imbecility*. Shuttleworth, to get away from the controversial racial allusion, suggested in 1866 the term "unfinished children." Until 1899, the only publications about the disease — and extremely few at that — came from Great Britain and the United States. Jones dealt in 1890 with the special features of the mouth and jaw. Oliver (Pennsylvania) described the ocular symptoms in 1891. Smith, in 1896, studied the configuration of the hands. Garrod discussed in 1898 the relationship between mongolism and congenital heart disease.

In 1899, Neumann was the first to mention mongolism on the European Continent. When he presented fifteen cases, Virchow vehemently denied that such an entity existed and declared that those were examples of what other authors had described as congenital rickets or as sporadic cretinism. The first report in France came from Bourneville in 1901, in Austria from Kassowitz in 1902, in Norway from Holmboe in 1905, in Russia from Kowalewsky in 1906.

"During the following years," to quote Oster, "mongolism became universally accepted as a clinical entity. An enormous amount of literature has been published on the disease, which has been observed in many people and races."

References

Benda, C. E.: *Mongolism and Cretinism*. New York, Grune and Stratton. 1946.

Bourneville, P.: *Idiotie du type mongolien*. Comte rendu de Bicêtre, 1901, pp. 137-147.

Brousseau, K.: *Mongolism*. A Study of the Physical and Mental

Characteristics of Mongolian Imbeciles. Revised by H. G. Brainerd. Baltimore, Williams & Wilkins. 1928. (Extensive bibliography).

Crookshank, F. G.: *The Mongol in Our Midst*. London, Kegan Paul. 1924.

Down, J. L. H.: Observations on an Ethnic Classification of Idiots. London Hosp. Reports, 1866, 3, 25. — *J. Ment. Sci.*, *13*:121-123, 1867.

—————: *On the Education and Training of the Feeble-in-Mind*. London, Lewis. 1876.

Fraser, J., and Mitchell, A.: Kalmuc Idiocy; Report of a Case with Autopsy and Notes on 62 Cases. *J. Ment. Sci.*, *22*:161-162; 169-179, 1876.

Garrod, A. E.: Cases Illustrating the Association of Congenital Heart Disease with Mongolian Form of Idiocy. *Brit. Med. J.*, *1*:1200; *2*, 1255, 1898.

Holmboe, M.: (Case demonstration). Forh. i det med. Selskab, Oslo, 1905, p. 233.

Jones, R.: The Mouth of Backward Children of the Mongol Type. *J. Ment. Sci.*, *36*:187, 1890.

Kassowitz, M.: Infantiles Myxödem, Mongolismus und Mikromelie. *Wien. med. Wochenschr.*, *52*:1106, 1202, 1256, 1302, 1358, 1451, 1902.

Kowalewsky, P. J.: Type Mongol de l'idiotie. *Ann. méd. psych.*, *4*:431-440, 1906.

Neumann, H.: Über den mongoloiden Typus der Idiotie. Berlin. *klin. Wochenschr.*, *30*:210, 1899.

Oliver, C. A.: A Clinical Study of the Ocular Symptoms Found in the So-called Mongolian Type of Idiocy. Transactions of the Amer. Ophthalmol. Soc., 1891, 6, 140-148.

Oster, J.: *Mongolism*. Copenhagen, Danish Science Press. 1953. (Extensive bibliography).

Seguin, E.: *Idiocy and its Treatment by the Physiological Method*. New York, W. Wood & Co., 1866, p. 381.

Shuttleworth, G. E.: Mongolian Imbecility. *Brit. Med. J.*, *2*:661-665, 1909.

Smith, T.: A Peculiarity in the Shape of the Hands in Idiots of the Mongolian Type. *Pediatrics*, *2*:315, 1896.

Suchsland, O.: *Die mongoloide Idiotie*. Halle, Karl Pritschow. 1909.

EMERGENCE OF ETIOLOGICAL CLASSIFICATIONS

Down did not seem to realize that his discovery of a thitherto unknown anomaly was in itself a major event and that, moreover, it signified a departure from the notion of the homogeneity of the feebleminded. His was the first link in a long — and as yet not completed — chain of attempts to single out and delineate disparate entities in which intellectual shortcomings are a common denominator.

In the medical past, there are several examples of the transition from age-old generalizations to the splitting off of diffuse concepts into a variety of specific categories. The advent of bacteriology did away with the assumption of a unity of all fevers and rendered the treatises *de febribus* and *de pestibus* meaningful mainly as historically significant documents. The idea of the homogeneity of "the insane," though punctured by individual observers sporadically since the days of antiquity, did not receive its final death blow until the second half of the 19th Century. A similar fate is at present anticipated — and has been prophetically envisioned by Eugen Bleuler — with regard to the concept of schizophrenia. We now also speak less of "epilepsy" and more of "the epilepsies." Before such changes occurred, the community of phenomena manifest, as it were, to the naked eye (chills, grossly erratic behavior, or convulsions) was deemed sufficient to make one think in terms of basic pathological identity.

The same kind of attitude prevailed when, less than two hundred years ago, mental retardation, recognized in its most conspicuous forms, began to engage professional attention. If one may paraphrase Gertrude Stein, the feebleminded were the feebleminded were the feebleminded. As a group, they were distinguished from those patients whose condition was titled dementia in contrast to amentia or idiocy. As Esquirol (1772-1840) put it, "a person with dementia is deprived of possessions he has once enjoyed, a rich man who has become poor; the idiot has aways been in misfortune and misery. The state of a demented person may vary, that of the idiot is always the same."

If any grouping of the mentally retarded was tried at all,

it pertained to differences in degree rather than in cause and pathology. Even the one known specific variety, cretinism, was viewed mostly as the severest stage of amentia. Thus, Feuchtersleben defined cretinism as "the extreme degree of idiotism with simultaneous somatic degeneration and endemic peculiarities."

Eventually, a not too clearly defined differentiation was made between idiots and imbeciles. Though no clear-cut statement can be offered about the time when this was introduced or about any one person who introduced it, it is safe to say that it entered into the literature following suggestions made by Belhomme and by Voisin and acquired popularity with the help cf Esquirol, who used language as the principal criterion: An imbecile is a mental defective who can communicate verbally; of idiots, there are three classes: 1) Those who can use a few words and short sentences; 2) Those who can utter monosyllables and grunts; 3) Those who have no language at all.

Around the middle of the 19th Century, probably under the influence of neurological refinements and a growing number of autopsy reports, the thought of a possible multiplicity of causes began to gain ground and the need for a classification other than on a quantitative basis made itself perceptible. Down, even before his description of mongolism, tried to subdivide idiocy in terms of causation. He stated: "The best classification of idocy, the one which most assists in the prognosis and treatment, is that which is based on its etiology." He distinguished accordingly between three major groups:

1. *Congenital idiocy* — those who have never possessed ordinary mental power, the defect being present at birth. In this category were the strumous, microcephalic, macrocephalic, hydrocephalic, eclampsic, epileptic, paralytic, and choreic.

2. *Developmental idiocy* — deterioration after a satisfactory start because of "proclivity to mental breakdown during a developmental crisis" (dentition or puberty). This can be eclampsic, epileptic, or choreic.

3. *Accidental idiocy* — the organism, originally free from any existing or potential defect, is assailed by injury or illness. This

group is subdivided into traumatic, inflammatory, and epileptic.

It has been said that Down — who in a way said so himself — had come upon the discovery of mongolism as a result of his plan to work out an ethnic classification (Caucasian, Ethiopian, Mongolian, Negroid). It seems more likely that, in the days of the immediate impact of Darwin's publications, the facial features of those patients have led Down along the paths which he took in 1866. That this was going to be a strange interlude was indicated promptly by Ireland's critical comments when he spoke up in the discussion of the reports by Fraser and Mitchell. Nevertheless, Ireland did adopt the term mongolism, which thus has become and remained the accepted designation. Now and then, the theory of mongolism as a regression to the Mongolian race has stirred the fantasy of some impressionable writers. In 1924, Crookshank obtained much ephemeral publicity with the notion that "the mongol in our midst" represents an atavistic regression; his claim, seemingly reinforced by some measurements, had sufficient appeal to the laity to see the opus through three editions.

Down's divagation into pseudo-anthropology does not detract from his classical contributions, which include one of the earliest attempts at an etiological grouping. His system, however, was quickly superseded by that which determined the organization of the textbook by Ireland and which served as a model for several decades.

William Wetherspoon Ireland, born in Edinburgh October 27, 1832, the son of a publisher and through his paternal grandmother a lineal descendent of John Knox, graduated from the university of his home town in 1855. After a short stay in Paris, he became resident surgeon at Dumfries Infirmary. In August 1856, he was appointed assistant surgeon in the East India Company's service and attached to the Bengal horse artillery. During the siege of Delhi, he was wounded by a bullet which destroyed one eye and passed around the base of the skull to the ear on the opposite side; another bullet entered his shoulder and lodged in his back. Among the casualties listed in the East India Register he was recorded as "killed before Delhi" on August 26, 1857. He must have been forgiven for proving the document wrong; In 1859, he was retired from the service with a special pension which made it possible for him to regain his health in ten years spent partly in Madera and partly on the European Continent. On his return to England with a vast knowledge of languages (French, German, Italian, Spanish, Norse, and Hindustani), he was made medical superintendent of the Scottish National Institution for Imbecile Children at Larbert (founded in 1855). He held this position from 1869-1879. In 1880, he opened a private home for retarded children, first at Stirling, then at Prestonpans and Polton. He died May 17, 1909, having retired a few years previously after his wife's death.

Ireland was a very versatile man, interested in history, literature, psychology, philosophy, and medicine. From his pen came, in addition to his writings on mental deficiency, a considerable number of books, some written before he came to Larbert and some after he had left it. In 1861, he published *A History of the Siege of Delhi by an Officer Who Served There* (Edinburgh, A. & C. Black). In 1863, Ward & Loch, London, brought out the two volumes of *Randolph Methyl, a Story of Anglo-Indian Life.* Then came, in 1867, *Studies of a Wandering Observer* (London, Chapman & Hall). During the last twenty-five years of his life, he published *The Blot Upon the Brain — Studies in History and Psychology* (Edinburgh, Bell & Bradfute, 1885; New York, G. P. Putnam's Sons. 1886; discussion of hallucinations of Mohammed, Luther, and Joan of Arc, hereditary neuroses of the royal family of Spain, etc.); *Through the Ivory Gate — Studies in Psychology and History* (Ibid., 1889; reflections on Swedenborg, William Blake, Ludwig II of Bavaria, Louis Riel, et. al); *Golden Bullets, a Story of the Days of Akber and Elizabeth* (Ibid., 1891); *The Life of Sir Henry Vane the Younger, with the History of the Events of His Time* (London, Eveleigh Nash. 1905). He also was a frequent contributor to the Journal of Mental Science, which printed his essays on Torquato Tasso, Auguste Comte, and Friedrich Nietzsche.

Such was the man who, almost by accident, stumbled into the occupation with mentally deficient children. Once he entered upon the field, he put, as the dates of the enumerated publications show, all other interests aside and devoted himself whole-heartedly to the specialty for which he had been called upon to function mainly as an administrator. Within a few years, he came to be respected as one of the foremost authorities. In 1877, less than a decade after his first contact with the problem, he published *On Idiocy and Imbecility*, which without reservation may be looked upon as the first well-organized and medically oriented textbook of mental deficiency. After extensive study of the psychiatric literature, he came to the following conclusion: "Idiocy and imbecility have usually been regarded by writers on insanity as pathological generalizations incapable of further subdivision." In his book, he set out to remedy this. He had twelve subdivisions: 1) Genetous idiocy; 2) Microcephalic idiocy; 3) Eclampsic idiocy; 4) Epileptic idiocy; 5) Hydrocephalic idiocy; 6) Paralytic idiocy; 7) Traumatic idiocy; 8) Inflammatory idiocy; 9) Sclerotic idiocy; 10) Syphilitic idiocy; 11) Cretinism; 12) Idiocy by deprivation.

While Down and Ireland established a new direction in the quest for an etiological grouping of mental defectives, the desire for a classification according to degree was by no means abolished. We thus witness two parallel groupings, which Weygandt characterized as follows: 1) from the practical viewpoint of educability and social behavior; 2) from the viewpoint of a purely scientific consideration of the nature of the manifold conditions.

The first, which has been a guide to educators to this day, has taken its cue from Belhomme and Esquirol (though the criterion of language has been abandoned). There have been variants: Howe, for instance, distinguished between "idiots, fools, and simpletons." Ziehen spoke of "idiocy, imbecility, and debility." The introduction of psychometry, which will be discussed in a later chapter, brought a refinement of these gradations on the basis of quantitative measurements.

Most of the medically trained writers of textbooks of mental deficiency followed along the road paved by Ireland. As time went on, more and more specific categories were discovered. Whereas, only two varieties, cretinism and mongolism, were known around 1870 (with occasional references to micro-cephaly), an increasing number of disease entities associated with more or less intellectual stunting were observed, described, and named since then.

By the end of the 19th Century, the advances in neurology had made possible the identification of a number of specific anomalies in which the mental defect was viewed as an integral part, as one of the several manifestations, of a circumscribed organic condition.

Tuberosclerosis, Pelizaeus-Merzbacher disease, and amaurotic family idiocy are representative examples of the discoveries made before 1900.

In 1863, von Recklinghausen described an infant who showed a combination of sclerotic areas in the brain and a rhabdomyoma of the heart. His report received little attention until in 1880 Bourneville made the profession aware of the condition, which he named tuberous sclerosis. In 1890, Pringle presented a case of "congenital adenoma sebaceum." In 1908, H. Vogt established the triad of convulsions, sebaceous adenoma, and mental defect as the essential ingredients of the disease, which has been variously referred to in the literature as Bourneville's disease, Pringle's disease, adenoma sebaceum, tuberosclerosis (the generally adopted name), and epiloia.

In 1885, Pelizaeus reported a heredofamilial anomaly consisting of chronic, diffuse degeneration of cerebral white matter. In 1910, Merzbacher added to the knowledge of this disease, which he called aplasia axialis extracorticalis congenita. While the first symptoms (nystagmus and tremors) start during the first months of life, "somewhere about the end of the sixth year, it usually becomes evident that the child is becoming demented." (Ford).

In 1887, Sachs published a clinical and pathological study of infantile cerebromacular degeneration which he explained as a congenital defect of development and which he called amaurotic family idiocy. The retinal changes which are found in this condition had been described in 1881 by the British ophthalmologist, Warren Tay. Hence, the name Tay-Sachs disease has been used frequently as a synonym.

Bourneville, Pelizaeus, Sachs and others thus set a pattern of demonstrating that there were forms of mental deficiency closely associated with a variety of specific structural anomalies of the central nervous system. Without particularly intending to do so, they inaugurated an era of searching for more such clearly definable disorders related to, or differing from, the few already known. New discoveries came in quick succession and, almost tumbling over each other, have been customarily named after the discoverers. New advances in biochemistry joined those in neurology. All this went on mostly in the stillness of scientific laboratories and it took several decades before such work became part of a general research plan for the study and prevention of mental deficiency.

References

Down, J. H. L.: Ethnic Classification of Idiots. Clinical Lecture Reports, London Hospital, 1866, 3, 259.
————: *On Some Mental Afflictions of Children and Youth.* London, Churchill. 1887.
Bourneville, D. M.: Scléreuse tubereuse des convulsions cérébrales. Idiotie et épilepsie hemiplégique. *Arch. de Neurol.* (Paris), *1*:69, 91, 391, 1880.
————, et D'Oller, H.: *Recherches sur l'épilepsie, l'hysterie at l'idiotie.* Paris. Delahaye. 1881.
Feuchtersleben, E. von: *Lehrbuch der ärztlichen Seelenkunde.* Wien, C. Gerold, 1845, p. 329.
Ford, F. R.: *Diseases of the Nervous System in Infancy, Childhood, and Adolescence,* Springfield, Thomas. Fourth edit., 1960, p. 832.
Ireland, W. W.: *On Idiocy and Imbecility.* London, Churchill. 1877.
Merzbacher, L.: Eine eigenartige familiär-hereditäre Erkrankungsform. *Ztschr. f. d. ges. Neurol. u. Psychiatrie, 3*:1-138, 1910.
Pelizaeus, F.: Über eine eigentümliche Form spastischer Lähmung mit Cerebralerscheinungen auf hereditärer Grundlage. *Arch. f. Psychiat. und Nervenkrankh. 16*:698-710, 1885.
Pringle, J. J.: A Case of Congenital Adenoma Sebaceum. *Brit. J. Dermatol.,* 1891, p. 1.
Recklinghausen, F. von: *Verh. Berl. Geburtshülfl. Gesellsch.* 1863, p. 73.

Sachs, B. A.: Family Form of Idiocy, Generally Fatal, Associated with Early Blindness. *J. Nerv. and Ment. Diseases,* 23:475-479, 1896.

Tay, W.: Symmetrical Changes in the Region of the Yellow Spot in Each Eye of an Infant. Transact. of the Ophthalmol. Soc. of London, 1881, 1, 55.

Vogt, H.: Zur Pathologie und pathologischen Anatomie der verschiedenen Idiotenformen: II. Tuberöse Sklerose. *Monatschr. f. Psychiat. und Neurol.,* 24:106-150, 1908.

Chapter 7

Special Classes in Public Schools

I n 1820, about twenty years before Guggenbühl's proclamations and the establishment of residential facilities for the education of mental defectives, a German teacher, acknowledging Pestalozzi as his mentor, published a pamphlet in which he advocated teaching as a means of amelioration. He suggested as major objectives the training of sense perception and "the awakening of reason (*Vernunft*) generally." The man was Johann Traugott Weise (born April 17, 1793, at Aue near Zeitz; died November 19, 1859). The pamphlet had the title (translated): Thoughts about feebleminded children, with regard to varieties, basic causes, manifestations, and ways of getting at them easily by means of education (Zeitz, Webelsche Buchhandlung. 1820). One year after its appearance, it was translated into Hollandish by H.W.C.A. Visser (Amsterdam, J.G.A. Beijerinck. 1821). This is probably the earliest document which deals concretely with a plan calculated to provide instruction for mentally deficient children.

It is difficult to ascertain whether and to what extent Weise's plea and outlined methods led to any kind of practical application. It seems that Weise's pamphlet received little attention and would have remained unknown if it had not been rediscovered and reproduced by Kirmsse ninety-one years after its publication. With the start and spread of institutional care, all thoughts about the education of mental defectives centered around instruction

Betrachtung

über

Geistesschwache Kinder

in

Hinsicht der Verschiedenheit, Grundursachen, Kennzeichen und der Mittel ihnen auf leichte Art durch Unterricht beizukommen.

Mit besonderer Rücksicht auf die Pestalozzi'sche Rechnenmethode

von

Traugott Weise,

Organist an der St. Nicolai = Kirche und zweiter Lehrer der Töchterschule in Zeitz.

Zeitz, 1820.

In der Webelschen Buchhandlung.

Title page of Weise's pamphlet on the education of retarded children. (Obtained through the generosity of the librarian of the Zentralsekretariat Pro Juventute in Zurich, Switzerland.)

in residential settings. When these were well on the way, it must have occurred to many educators that after removal of those who were conspicuously defective there were still pupils in their classrooms who could not apply themselves to the prescribed curriculum. Around 1860, voices were heard which began to advocate special facilities for such children within the framework of public school instruction.

On September 28, 1859, Haupt, the principal of a school in Halle, proposed at a meeting of the school board "to form a special class for defective children, now numbering seventeen, with possibly two hours (daily) for instruction." In 1860, a similar arrangement was started in Chemnitz.

In 1863, Karl Ferdinand Kern, whom we have met as the founder of one of the earliest German institutions (1847), delivered before the pedagogical society in Leipzig a lecture on the education and care of defective children; he recommended special schools for those who, not in need of institutional placement, still could not keep up with others in the regular schools.

One year later, Stötzner published a pamphlet "on schools for children of deficient capacity; — first draft of a plan for establishing the same." To give emphasis to this 43-page appeal, Kern and Stötzner jointly founded a Society for the Advancement of the Education of Mentally Defective Children (which did not last long); in 1865, on the occasion of the meeting of the German Teacher's Association in Leipzig, they formed a section for "pedagogical hygiene."

Stötzner's plan to start such a school in Leipzig did not materialize, however, even after the praise it received at the 1865 meeting of the German scientists and physicians (*Versammlung der deutschen Naturforscher und Ärzte*) in Hanover. Parents resented the idea of having their children "branded" by removing them to a separate building. Besides, the officials were averse to such a move as too drastic a step, since the aim at that time was regarded as one of training those children temporarily apart from their classmates and ultimately restoring a large percentage of them to their regular classes.

These considerations led to a return to the practice begun by Haupt. Special classes in the ordinary schools had a greater appeal to the authorities and to the public than concentration in units away from the rest of the school population. In 1867, the school board of Dresden brought about the establishment of an "Auxiliary Class" (*Hilfsklasse*) for sixteen children. Gera and Elberfeld followed in the 1870's; Brunswick and Leipzig in 1881: Dortmund and Halberstadt in 1883; Königsberg and Krefeld in 1885; Cologne in 1886; Aachen, Düsseldorf, Kassel, and Lübeck in 1888; Altona, Bremen, and Frankfurt am Main in 1889; Breslau and Hamburg in 1892; Görlitz in 1893; Karlsruhe in 1896; Pforzheim in 1897; Darmstadt in 1899; Munich in 1902; Heidelberg in 1908; Stuttgart in 1911. (Compiled by Homburger). By 1905, 181 German cities had 583 classes (81 in Berlin alone), enrolling 6,623 boys and 5,300 girls .

Norway, with the first special class organized in Oslo in 1874, seems to have been the first country to follow the trend begun in Germany.

Switzerland came next; though Basel and Bern each claimed the credit for being first in 1888, they were, according to Mindlin, preceded by Chur (Coire) in 1881. In 1898, the Swiss Public Welfare Society (*Schweizerische Gemeinnützige Gesellschaft*) established a course of instruction for teachers of special classes, which was begun in Zurich in the academic year 1899-1900. In 1907, Switzerland had sixty-nine special classes, serving 1,415 pupils.

In England, a special school was opened in 1892 in London. A so-called "permissive act" of 1899 left the matter to the discretion of the communities which at their pleasure could or could not adopt the statutory regulations for auxiliary school instruction.

In Austria, special schooling was first considered in 1895, when a department for defective school-age children was organized as a part of the public school administration. Progress, however, was slow; Maennel in 1905 quoted a contemporary critic as saying: "Austria has only half as many classes as the city of Hamburg. The great majority of her abnormal children are without any instruction at all or remain as a burden upon the general public schools."

In Denmark, Copenhagen started an auxiliary school in 1900. In the same year, in Sweden, the teachers of Stockholm directed the attention of the school authorities to those "abnormal children who are hindered in their development."

In Italy, Sante de Sanctis, who later published the famous textbook *Neuropsichiatria infantile,* started in 1899 in Rome an "asylum school for weakminded children," a day home for about forty pupils.

During all that time, nothing was stirring in France. In 1904, in an essay, *Pour les enfants anormaux,* which appeared in the *Manuel général de l'instruction primaire,* the author (quoted by Maennel) exclaimed: "The most autocratically ruled states of Europe have made instruction democratic, and have opened schools for all their subjects, in which nervous, deaf and dumb, or idiotic, as well as healthy children, can be instructed. With us, the opposite is the case; while our scholars were the first to point out the means to alleviate the natural defects of mankind, the teaching of abnormals has become so exclusive that the families concerned are often compelled to permit their children to grow up as chance wills." It seems that the "scholars" could not prevail on their compatriots sufficiently to get the actions they felt were needed. In 1898, Bourneville published a monograph which not only urged the creation of special classes but also contained the outlines of a program of teaching. Yet it was not until 1909 that the first special class was started in Paris.

In the United States, sporadic efforts began in 1878 (1874? 1879?), when two such classes were opened in Cleveland. In many instances, it is not quite possible to be exactly correct about the dates. Both Wallin and Davies encountered similar difficulties. Wallin remarked: "There are discrepancies in the dates reported; these could be cleared up by wading through the original school reports." Davies found that "the dates of establishment and character of special classes are in some instances uncertain." Wading through original entries does not help much because some recorded resolutions were not followed by immediate action and because some of the classes were begun as "disciplinary" units rather than intended for retarded children. It is commonly agreed that the first special class for defective children in this country was opened on November 30, 1896, in Providence, Rhode Island, under the auspices of the Superintendent of Schools, H. S. Tarbell. This was an outgrowth of the School for Special Discipline and Instruction which had been established in that city a few years previously (in the spring of 1894?). Springfield, Mass., came next in 1897; Chicago followed in 1898; Boston in 1899; New York in 1900; Philadelphia in 1901; Los Angeles in 1902; Detroit and Elgin, Ill., in 1903; Trenton, N. J., in 1905; Bridgeport, Conn., Newton, Mass., Rochester, N. Y., and Washington in 1906. Most of the larger cities followed in rapid succession. Maennel could announce in 1905 that "the idea has taken firm hold."

This is a far cry from the reception which the idea had received from the local press in Rhode Island when the special class was opened in 1896. Goddard reminisced: "The novelty and strangeness of the movement is well indicated by the fact that in Providence a certain newspaper reporter thought it was an excellent joke and wrote an elaborate account under the title of 'The Fool Class.' This designation was so obnoxious and was given such publicity that it set back the movement very decidedly in that city, for no one was willing to have his child placed in a class designated by such a name."

In 1905, the first training opportunity for teachers of special classes in this country was offered at the New Jersey Training School for Feebleminded Boys and Girls.

All these efforts antedated the great "breakthrough" by Binet and Simon whose introduction of mental testing inaugurated a new era of instruction based on tested ability of the individual pupil.

References

Baker, B. W.: History of the Care of the Feebleminded. *Bull. Mass. Dept. of Mental Diseases*, Vol. *XIV*, April 1930.

Bosbauer, H., Miklas, L., and Schiner, H.: *Handbuch der Schwachsinnigenfürsorge*. Leipzig, Teubner. 1905.

Bourneville, D. M.: Création des classes spéciales pour les enfants arriérés. Paris, publication du progrès médical. 1898.

Davies, S. P.: *Social Control of the Mentally Deficient*. New York, Crowell. 1939.

――――――: *The Mentally Retarded in Society*. New York, Columbia University Press. 1959, p. 176.

Frampton, N. E., and Rowell, H. G.: *Education of the Handicapped*. Vol I., History. Yonkers, World Book Co. 1938.

Goddard, H. H.: *School Training of Defective Children*. Yonkers, World Book Co. 1914.

Homburger, A.: *Psychopathologie des Kinderalters*. Berlin, Julius Springer. 1926, p. 146.

Kirmsse, M.: *Weises Betrachtungen über geistesschwache Kinder*. Ein Beitrag zur Geschichte der Heilpädagogik in der ersten Hälfte des 19. Jahrhunderts. Langensalza, Hermann Beyer & Söhne. 1911.

Maennel, B.: *Vom Hilfsschulwesen*. Sechs Vorträge. Leipzig, Teubner. 1905. (Translated by F. B. Dresslar. The Auxiliary Schools in Germany. Washington, U. S. Bureau of Education. Bull. No. 3. 1907.)

Mindlin, D. F.: Care for the Mentally Deficient in Switzerland. *Am. J. Ment. Deficiency, 51*:766-778, 1947.

Mitchell, D.: Schools and Classes for Exceptional Children. Cleveland, Survey Commission of Cleveland Foundation. 1916.

Reinke, W.: *Die Unterweisung und Erziehung schwachsinniger Kinder*. Berlin, Oehmigke. 1897.

Stötzner, H.: *Über Schulen fur schwachbefähigte Kinder*. Erster Entwurf zur Begründung derselben. Leipzig und Heidelberg, C. F. Winter. 1864.

Wallin, J. E. W.: *Education of Mentally Handciapped Children*. New York, Harper and Brothers. 1955, p. 18 (footnote).

Wintermann, A.: *Die Hilfsschulen Deutschlands und der deutschen Schweiz*. Langensalza, Hermann Beyer u. Söhne. 1898.

Chapter 8

Quantitative Determination of Intellectual Adequacy

T HE RECOGNITION OF intellectual paucity, when attention began to be paid to it, depended at first solely on crude observation. No diagnostic criteria were available beyond those which were obvious to "the naked eye." A person either was, or was not, considered mentally deficient. The classifications by Down and by Ireland pertained essentially, if not exclusively, to "idiots." Differentiations as to the degree of the defect leaned heavily on the presence or absence of language (Esquirol) or on a more or less arbitrary distinction between idiocy and imbecility. (Ireland stated in 1877 that "imbecility is a minor degree of mental deficiency than idiocy").

Little else could be expected at a time when neither physicians nor educators were familiar with the data of infantile development. Children just grew up, and that was that. Not until past the middle of the 18th Century did it occur to anyone that the science of man might include an inquiry into the gradual unfolding of the functions of locomotion, communication, perception, and socialization. The barest rudiments of anything remotely resembling a psychology of childhood, have been traced to Johann Amos Comenius (Komensky, 1592-1670), Moravian churchman and educator, who in several books, written in the turbulent years of the Thirty-Year War, advocated a graduated instruction in habits, diction, and grasp of the environment. John Locke (1632-1704), the English philosopher, spoke of "natural inclinations," as a basis for education. He insisted that, if education is to be based on native instincts and capacities, it becomes important to make a careful study of the child's equipment. Jean Jacques Rousseau's *Emile* (1762) contained, probably for the first time, a plea for the direct study of children and inaugurated an era of more or less naive, unsystematized jottings about the doings of the respective author's offspring during the initial stages of growth. Most of these biographic depositions, though marking the start of a new type of curiosity, still carried a heavy ballast of philosophic reflections, some admixture of mysticism, and conclusions based on pious idealism rather than on factual data. But, in the subsequent decades, the attention of the diarists was focussed increasingly on sober empiricism, beginning with Tiedemann's book in 1787 on the first four years of his children but not coming into full swing until the second half of the 19th Century. Sigismund in 1857, Darwin in 1877, Preyer in 1882, Perez in 1886, and others stripped their observations of diffuseness and unwarranted generalizations. Preyer's work has rightly been regarded as the beginning of modern child psychology. He observed and recorded systematically the development of his son from the moment of his birth every day until the end of the third year; he included notes on perception, space orientation, memory, voluntary actions, motility, and language, and offered for the first time an account of the gradually progressive differentiation and interdependence of early functions.

The work of the diarists was limited in scope to data gathered from only one child or, at the most, from a small number of siblings, invariably the offspring of highly sophisticated people. A desire to expand the information led Stanley Hall in the 1880's to ask thousands of parents to fill out questionnaires about actual observations of their children or reminiscences of their own childhood. At about the same time, Hall, preceded in this enterprise by a German educator (Bartholomäi, 1870), made a survey of what he called "the contents of children's minds" on entering school and presented the facts thus obtained in terms of percentage calculations. (In 1891, Hall founded the *Pedagogical Seminary*, a magazine devoted to the study of children).

Simultaneously, some investigators singled out specific phases of child development for phenomenologic and experimental studies. Detailed research was undertaken on motility (Fuchs 1896); perception (Kroner 1882; Genzmer 1882), language (Schleicher 1861; Egger 1870; Taine 1876; Holden 1877; Pollock 1878; Vierordt 1879; Schultze 1880; Humphreys 1880), and drawing ability (Barnes 1893).

Thus, following centuries of total neglect and stimulated by Locke, Rousseau, and a growing trend toward objectivity and unbiased inquiry, a sudden spurt led to the seeding and sprouting of developmental psychology. Sporadic beginnings burgeoned into a wealth of activities in the last three decades of the 19th Century. The groundwork was laid, questions were formulated, methods were worked out, and concerted efforts began to yield a few incontestable verities. The powers of political reactions and theological interference with the study of man had lost their grip. When, in 1851, the Prussian police closed Froebel's kindergartens on the pretense that they were hotbeds of atheism and socialism, the barrage of ridicule was too much for the rulers to endure, and the charge was withdrawn in 1860. When Compayré published in 1880 his famous manual of instruction, *dégagé de tout caractère confessionel* (completely disengaged from confessional issues), he was attacked vehemently on similar grounds; the attackers did not succeed in dislodging him from the position of honor bestowed on him by the French Republic.

The results obtained from diaries, questionnaires, and sporadic experiments called for the elaboration of a systematic procedure and the creation of a unified discipline. For this, a precedent had been set as far back as in 1859 by Adolf Kussmaul, an eminent physician, who in his study of newborn infants collected a sufficiently wide range of data from a sufficiently large number of children to allow him to arrive at some valid general conclusions.

Such was the state of affairs when Alfred Binet was appointed in 1904 by the French Minister of Public Instruction to study the means for the adequate schooling of retarded children. To be more specific, the task assigned to him was one of devising a method for selecting from the children in the schools of Paris those who could not adapt themselves to the curriculum and thereby reduced the efficiency of the teachers and the fellow pupils. There were no special classes in the public schools in France at that time but in the preparation of plans for their introduction it was deemed necessary to seek better criteria than those in existence for making proper assignments.

Alfred Binet was born in Nice July 11, 1857, the son of a physician. He went to Paris in 1871, studied law (which he never practiced) and medicine, and was drawn by 1880 toward clinical and experimental psychology. In 1889, he established at the Sorbonne the first psychology laboratory in his country and was made its director in 1894. He published many articles in *Revue philosophique, Revue scientifique,* and *Mind.* He founded and for many years edited the first French journal of psychology, *L'Année psychologique.* The scope of his interests, his spirit of scientific inquiry, and the volume of his literary productivity are truly amazing.

In his first book *La psychologie du raisonnement* (Paris, F. Alcan. 1886. — English translation by A. G. Whyte. Chicago and London, Kegan Paul. 1899), he applied the method of hypnotism to psychological questions. This was followed in 1887 by an extensive study of the same subject in conjunction with Charles Féré, *Le magnétisme animal* (Paris, F. Alcan. — English translation: London, Kegan Paul. 1877). In 1888, he published a collection of studies, *Etudes de psychologie expérimentale* (Paris, O. Doin. 1888; second edition, 1891), which deals with fetishism in love; the psychic life of micro-organisms; the intensity of mental images; hypnotism; handwriting in hysteria. Soon thereafter came a basic study in the realm of abnormal psychology, *Les altérations de la personalité* (Paris, F. Alcan. 1892. — English translation by H. G. Baldwin. London, Chapman & Hall. 1896). With the collaboration of Philippe, Courtier, and Henri, he then published the *Introduction à la psychologie expérimentelle* (Paris, F. Alcan. 1894). The same year brought forth a study of great "calculators" and chess players, *Psychologie des grands calculateurs et joueurs d'échecs* (Paris, Hachette. 1894). A book on suggestibility, *La suggestibilité,* appeared in 1900 (Paris, Schleicher frères, a publishing firm which in 1898 had brought out Binet's study on intellectual fatigue, done together with V. Henri).

Binet had a unique capacity for inspiring his colleagues and inviting them to work with him. When he noticed that a younger man, Théodore Simon, showed a great deal of interest in investigations of the development of intelligence in children, the two joined forces and began a period of collaboration which was to become a significant milestone in the history of educational psychology.

Théodore Simon was born in Dijon on July 10, 1873, the son of an engineer. Orphaned very early, he went to live with an uncle at Sens where he attended the lycée. He studied medicine in Paris and became interested in psychology, especially in Binet's work. Associating with Binet's studies of the relation between physical growth and intellectual development, he made his own investigations in the public schools and published the results in his doctoral thesis in 1900 (*Documents relatifs à la correlation entre le développement physique et la capacité intellectuelle*). He pursued his medical career at interne (1901-1903), associate attending psychiatrist (1904-1905), attending psychiatrist (1905-1920, interrupted temporarily by military service in World War I), director of the colony of Perray-Vancluse (1920-1930), and director of the Henri-Rousselle Hospital (1930-1936; 1939-1940). All the while, he carried on his work in the field of educational psychology, as the director of a pedagogical laboratory in Paris and professor at the Teachers College of the Seine, as an associate and collaborator of Binet, and later as professor of the French School of Anthropology until 1960. The French Government made him a member of the Legion of Honor. He died on September 4, 1961.

The names Binet and Simon, usually connected by a hyphen, have become household words in the psychologic, educational, and sociologic vocabularies. Ionel Rapaport, in a moving obituary

(*Am. J. Ment. Deficiency*, 1962, 67, 367-368) wrote: "It would be vain to dissociate Simon's name from that of Binet in the work they accomplished together, and to separate their individual contributions from their work in common."

It is well to remember that the primary purpose of the task assigned to Binet was to direct "a study of measures to be taken, showing the benefits of instruction for defective children." This was in a way, the practical application of some of the ideas cherished by Seguin who had declared hopefully: "The primary aim of classification is to attain a gauge of mental activity that shall facilitate learning." Indeed, the scope of the study went far beyond the original objective of selecting children who were in need of instruction in special classes. Binet, aided by Simon, examined thousands of children of different ages, presenting to them tasks of varying complexity. He tabulated the responses and thus determined statistically what the majority could do and could not do at a given age. He thus established a scale which set up a norm of performance. With the help of this procedure, it was possible to learn to what extent any *individual* child conformed to, or deviated from, the norm of average.

The first draft of the scale was made public in 1905. A revision came out in 1908. A third, improved, set was presented in 1911, the year in which Binet died.

Binet's work is of fundamental importance for several reasons. It brought into existence a concrete and reliable method of helping teachers to evaluate a child's "mental age," so that instruction might be adapted to his needs and grasp. Another enormous value lies in the fact that here for the first time a successful attempt was made to assess the heterogeneity of human beings, at least so far as receptiveness to classroom teaching was concerned.

But the "measuring scale of intelligence" by Binet and Simon had still another far-reaching effect, one which had been hardly anticipated at the outset. It became evident that intellectual inadequacy was not an absolute, all-or-none attribute, as had been previously assumed. There were gradations from the slightest deviation to the most profound state of deficiency. Between the "average" and the idiot-imbecile stood a huge contingent of "borderliners", who became known as morons.

The term "moron" was introduced by Goddard in 1910. He declared: "I presume no one in this audience, certainly none of the superintendents of institutions, need to be reminded that the public is entirely ignorant of this particular group. Our public school systems are full of them, and yet superintendents and boards of education are strugglnig to make normal people out of them. One of the most helpful things that we can do would be to distinctly mark out the limits of this class and help the general public understand that they are a special group and require special treatment, in institutions when possible, in special classes in public schools, when institutions are out of reach.

"Two words have been suggested for this group, the one being the word *proximate* with the underlying thought that these children are nearly normal. The other word proposed is a Greek word, the noun from the Greek word meaning foolish, *moronia,* and these children might be called *morons;* fool or foolish in the English sense exactly describes this group of children. The *Century Dictionary* defines a fool as one who is deficient in judgment, or sense, etc., which is distinctly the group we are working with. I believe the etymology is correct and the derivations would be easy. We would have moron for the noun, moronia for the condition, moronic for the adjective, and so it would seem to answer every requirement."

To quote Davies: "The 'moron' was an alarming discovery. Surveys indicated that thousands of his kind were to be found among the general population, generally unrecognized for what they were, and with practically no facilities for their training."

The "discovery of the moron", alarming as it was, brought a new dimension to the care and study of the mentally retarded. It was no longer sufficient to restrict the efforts to the establishment and improvement of institutional facilities. Intramural custody and education, a startling innovation, in the 1840's, was limited to the group which had been recognized as defective in the pre-Binet days. A sense of responsibility arose for the "in-betweeners" when the new tests showed them to be in such abundance. A vague notion that not all children who failed to progress scholastically should be shoved into institutions had existed before the publication of Binet's work and had led to the introduction of special classes in public schools, even though reliable criteria for the selection of pupils had not been available. But now that measurements made the task easier, the need for special education of children of less than average intelligence became a matter of public awareness.

Strangely enough, as in the past, France, the country which, like no other, has produced the great pioneers and pathfinders in the area of mental retardation, lagged far behind in the practical utilization of the new ideas and methods and left it to others to reap the harvest. In Germany, Bobertag's adaptation of the Binet tests, published in 1914, gave rise to a whole series of studies and served as a guide to the group which, under the name of *Heilpädagogik* (remedial education), had combined German, Austrian, and Swiss educators in a common effort to help handicapped children. In Belgium, Decroly and Degand presented a critical review of the Binet-Simon tests as early as in 1907. Decroly's student, Descoeudres, published in Switzerland a synopsis of the test in 1915.

In this country, the tests were first made known by Henry Herbert Goddard. Born 1866 in Vassalboro, Maine, and educated at Haverford College, he was appointed professor of psychology at the State Normal School of Pennsylvania and in the fall of 1906 he took charge of the department of psychological research of the Training School at Vineland, New Jersey. On a trip to Europe in the spring of 1908, Goddard learned of Binet's work. On his return, he tried the tests in Vineland and, as he wrote, "experience with these tests has continually reassured us not only as to their value but as to their amazing accuracy; their usefulness as a means of understanding the mental development of children is beyond question, and we confidently believe that the time will speedily come when every child in school will be occasionally examined by some such method as this with a view of determining his actual mental development, and consequently what can be expected of him." Goddard published a brief account of the 1905 tests in 1908 and in 1910 an abstract of the 1908 scale.

References

Ament, K. W.: *Begriff und Begriffe der Kindessprache.* Berlin, Reuther and Reichard. 1902.

——————:*Fortschritte der Kindesseelenkunde.* Leipzig, Engelmann. 1904. (Extensive bibliography).

Barnes, E.: A study of Children's Drawings. *Pedag. Semin.*, 2:451-463, 1893.

Bartholomäi, F.: Der Vorstellungskreis der Berliner Kinder beim Eintritt in die Schule. Berlin und seine Entwicklung. Städtisches Jahrbuch für Volkswirtschaft und Statistik, 1870, 4, 59-77. — English translation in Reports of U. S. Committee on Education for Year 1900-1901. Washington, U. S. Printing Office 1902.

Binet, A.: *Étude expérimentale de l'intelligence.* Paris, Schleicher frères. 1903.

Binet, A., et Simon, T.: *Les Enfants anormaux.* Guide pour l'admission des enfants anormaux dans les classes de perfectionnement. Paris. A. Collin. 1907.

——————: *Le mesure du développement de' l'intelligence chez les jeunes enfants.* Paris, A. Coneslant. 1911.

Blair, G. M.: Educational Psychology, Its Development and Present Status. Univ. of Illinois Bulletin, Urbana. 1948.

Bobertag, O.: Intelligenzprüfung nach Binet-Simon-Bobertag. (8 pages). Halle, Marhold. 1914.

Brockett, L. P.: (Philobiblius). *History and Progress of Education, from the Earliest Time to the Present.* New York, A. S. Barnes and Burr. 1860.

Champneys, F. H.: Notes on an Infant. *Mind*, 6:104-107, 1881.

Darwin, C.: Biographical Sketch of an Infant. *Mind*, 2:285-294, 1877.

Decroly, O., and Degand, J.: Les tests de Binet et Simon pour la mesure de l'intelligence. Contribution critique. *Arch. de psychol.*, 6:27-130, 1907.

Dennis, W.: Historical Beginnings of Child Psychology. *Psychol. Bulletin*, 46:224-239, 1949.

Descoeudres, A.: Les tests de Binet- Simon comme mesure du développement des enfants anormaux. (30 pages). Geneva, Kundig. 1915.

Egger, M. E.: *Observations et reflexions sur le développement d'intelligence et de langage chez les enfants.* Paris, Picard. 1870.

Fuchs, A.: *Die Unruhe.* Gütersloh, Bertelsmann. 1896.

Genzmer, A.: *Untersuchungen über die Sinneswahrnehmungen des neugeborenen Menschen.* Halle, Max Niemeyer. 1882.

Goddard, H. H.: Four Hundred Classified by the Binet Method. *J. Psycho-Asthenics, 15*:17-30, 1910.

Hall, G. S.: Contents of Children's Minds. *Princeton Review, 11*:249-272, 1883; *Pedag. Sem., 1*:139-173, 1891.

Holdren, E. S.: On the Vocabularies of Children Under Two Years of Age. Transactions Am. Philolog. Asso., 1877, pp. 58-68.

Humphreys, M. W.: *A Contribution to Infantile Linguistics.* Hartford, Case, Lockwood & Brainard. 1880.

Kroner, T.: Über die Sinnesempfindungen der Neugeborenen. *Breslauer ärztl. Ztsch., 4*:37-41, 1882.

Kussmaul, A.: *Untersuchungen über das Seelenleben des neugeborenen Menschen.* Leipzig & Heidelberg, C. E. Winter. 1859.

Lange, K.: *Der Vorstellungskreis unserer sechsjährigen Kleinen.* Allgem. Schulzeitung, 1879, 56, 327 ff.

Löbisch, I. E.: *Entwicklungsgeschichte der Seele des Kindes.* Wien, Haas. 1851.

Major, D. R.: *First Steps in Mental Growth.* New York, Macmillan. 1906.

Murphy, G.: *Historical Introduction to Modern Psychology.* New York, Harcourt, Brace. 1949. Chapter XXVI, Child Psychology, pp. 389-401.

Perez, B.: *La psychologie de l'enfant. Les trois premières années de l'enfant.* Paris. 1878. English translation by Alice M. Christie. The First Three Years of Childhood. London, Sonnenschein. 1885, and Chicago, Marquis. 1885.

—————: *La psychologie de l'enfant. l'enfant de trois à sept ans.* Paris, F. Alcan. 1886.

Pollock, F.: An Infant's Progress in Language. *Mind, 3*:392-401, 1878.

Preyer, W.: *Die Seele des Kindes.* Beobachtungen über die geistige Entwicklung des Menschen in den ersten Lebensjahren. Leipzig, T. Grieben, 1882.

Quetelet, L. A. J.: *Sur l'homme et le développement de ses facultés ou essai de physique sociale.* Paris, Bachdier. 1835.

Schleicher, A.: Einige Beobachtungen an Kindern. *Beiträge zur vergleichenden Sprachforschung,* 2:497-498, 1861. (Dennis: "Probably the first to record the speech development of a specific child").

Schultze, F.: *Die Sprache des Kindes. Eine Anregung zur Erforschung des Gegenstandes.* Leipzig, Gunther. 1880.

Scupin, E. & G.: *Bubis erste Kindheit.* Leipzig, Grieben. 1907.

—————: *Bubi im 4-6. Lebensjahre. Ibid.* 1910.

Shinn, M .W.: *Notes on the Development of a Child.* Univ. Calif. Publications, 1893-1899.

—————: *Development of the Senses.* Univ. Calif. Press. 1907.

Sigismund, B.: *Kind und Welt.* Braunschweig, Vieweg. 1856.

Strumpell, L.: *Notizen über die geistige Entwicklung eines weiblichen Kindes während der ersten zwei Lebensjahre.* Leipzig, Georg Böhme. 1880.

Sully, J.: Babies and Science. *Cornhill Magazine,* 43:539-554, 1881.

Taine, H.: Note sur l'acquisition de langage chez les enfants et dans l'espèce humaine. *Revue philos.,* 1:3-23,1876. (Translated in *Mind* 2:252-257, 1877.)

Tiedemann, F.: Beobachtungen über die Entwicklung der Seelenfähigkeiten des Kindes. Hessische Beiträge zur Gelehrsamkeit und Kunst, 1787, 2, 313 ff; 3, 486 ff. (Republished by Ufer, Altenburg, 1897-56 pages). — English translation by S. Langer & C. Murchison, *J. Genet. Psychol.,* 34:205-230, 1927.

Vierordt, K.: Die Sprache des Kindes. *Deusche Revue,* 4:29-46, 1879.

Chapter 9

The Eugenic Scare

I N THE EARLY days of active interest in mental deficiency, there were occasional references to heredity as a cause. These were offered unemotionally as assumptions, as the results of general observations not based on statistical data. The main emphasis centered around the retarded individuals themselves.

In 1865, Sir Francis Galton expressed in rather sweeping terms his concern about the destiny of the human race. Unchecked fertility of the unfit was presented as a threat to be averted by programs calculated to reduce their birth rate. In 1883, Galton introduced the concept of eugenics (a term coined by him) as "the science which deals with all influences that improve the inborn qualities of a race."

A few years previously, in July 1874, Dugdale, a penologist, had been deputed by the Prison Association of New York to visit county jails and State prisons and to "report thereon." He found six persons under different family names "who turned out to be blood relations in some degree." These six persons "belonged to a long lineage, reaching back to the early colonists, who had lived in the same locality for generations and were so despised by the reputable community that their family name had come to be used generically as a term of reproach." Dugdale made a genealogical survey which was published in 1877 under the title *The Jukes, a Study in Crime, Pauperism, Disease and Heredity.* The family descended from the two sons of a backwoodsman, called Max, who married two of the five Jukes sisters (Jukes is a fictitious name.) Information was obtained about 709 out of 1200 descendants. Of these, 140 had been imprisoned for crime, 280 were paupers dependent on public support, and the majority were of low physical and moral standard. Elisha Harris, M.D., corresponding secretary of the Prison Association, wrote an introduction to the book; in it he called attention to "the social hades of the dangerous classes." Dugdale himself made no special reference to mental deficiency. His book was reprinted in 1910. In 1915, Estabrook of the Department of Experimental Evolution of the Carnegie Institution made a follow-up investigation during which "every Juke possible to see has been personnally visited." Though there is no evidence of any attempted intellectual assessment (tests being available since 1910), the author asserted that "not all feebleminded Jukes are criminal, but all the Juke criminals that I have known I regard as mentally defective" and that "one-half of the Jukes were and are feebleminded."

Fourteen years after the first publication of Dugdale's book, the Reverend O. C. McCulloch presented at the 15th Annual Session of the National Conference of Charities and Correction, held in Buffalo, the story of the "tribe of Ishmael." He acknowledged that his report "resembles the study of Dr. Dugdale into the Jukes, and was suggested by that." This was a family "with a pauper history of several generations and so intermarried with others as to form a pauper ganglion of several hundreds." McCulloch referred to them as "decaying stock" and a "festering mass." There was no special allusion to mental deficiency but this seemed to be implied. "What can we do?" the Reverend asked. His answer was:

"First, we must close up official out-door relief.

"Second, we must check private and indiscriminate benevolence, falsely so called.

"Third, we must get hold of the children."

In 1905, the Swiss psychiatrist Jörger rounded up a family of vagrants, whom he called Zeros, as a sample of hereditary transmission. In 1919, he gave a similar account of the "Family Markus," one of whose female ancestors had been married to one of the Zero ancestors. In both family groups there were said to be 20 per cent imbeciles.

In 1911, Charles B. Davenport declared categorically: "Two mentally defective parents will produce only mentally defective offspring. This is the first law of inheritance of mental ability . . . The second law of heredity of mentality is that, aside from 'mongolians,' probably no imbecile is born except of parents who, if not mentally defective themselves, both carry mental defect in their germ plasm . . . In view of the certainty that all of the children of two feebleminded parents will be defective, how great is the folly, yes, the crime, of letting two such persons marry!"

In 1912, Goddard brought notoriety to a famliy known by the fictitious name Kallikak. The story of the Kallikaks kindled a spark which soon burst into flames and drove a number of volunteer firefighters to frantic activity.

"One bright October day . . . there came to the Training School at Vineland a little eight year old girl. She had been born in an almshouse." A field worker (Miss Elizabeth S. Kite) was assigned to trace Deborah's ancestral background. The great-great-great-grandfather, Martin, joined a military company at the beginning of the Revolution. In a tavern, he met a feebleminded girl by whom he became the father of a feebleminded son, Martin Kallikak, Jr. "From him have come 480 descendants; 143 of these, we have conclusive proof were or are feebleminded while only forty-six have been found normal. The rest are unknown or doubtful. Among these 480 descendants, thirty-six have been illegitimate; there have been thirty-three sexually immoral persons, mostly prostitutes; there have been twenty-four confirmed alcoholics; there have been three epileptics; eighty-two died in infancy; three were criminals; eight kept houses of ill fame. These people have married into other families, generally of about the same type, so that we now have on record and charted 1,146 individuals. Of this large group, we have discovered that 262 were feebleminded, while 197 were considered normal, the remaining 581 being still undetermined."

The same Martin Kallikak, "on leaving the Revolutionary

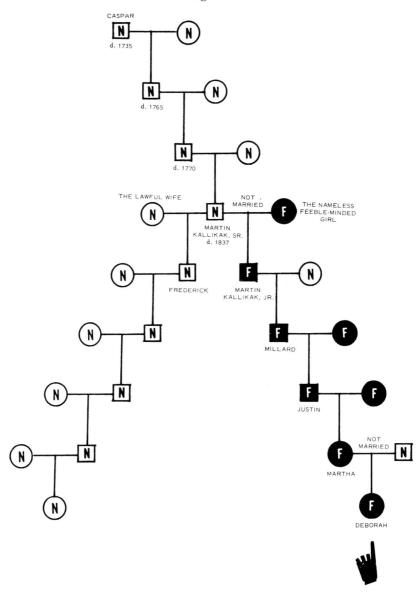

Genealogical Chart of the Kallikaks. N = Normal; F = Feebleminded; □ = Male; O = Female. (From H. H. Goddard: *The Kallikak Family.* New York, Macmillan, 1912. "[This chart] shows the line of descent of the Kallikak family from their first colonial ancestors. It was Martin who divided

(Continued on next page)

Army, straightened up and married a respectable girl of good family, and through this union has come another line of descendants of radically different character. These now number 496 in direct descent . . . All of the legitimate children of Martin Sr. married into the best families in their state, the descendents of colonial governors, signers of the Declaration of Independence, soldiers, and even the founders of a great university. Indeed, in this family and its collateral branches, we find nothing but good representative citizenship. There are doctors, lawyers, judges, educators, traders, landholders, in short, respectable citizens, men and women prominent in every phase of social life."

The name Kallikak, invented by Goddard, stems from a combination of two Greek words: *kalos*, meaning attractive, pleasing, and *kakos*, meaning bad, evil. Thus the name was to symbolize the two lines of the descendants of Martin Sr., one respectable, intelligent, well adjusted, and the other worthless, a blot on society.

Goddard concluded: "Feeblemindedness is hereditary and transmitted as surely as any other character. We cannot successfully cope with these conditions until we recognize feeblemindedness and its hereditary nature, recognize it early, and take care of it. In considering the question of care, segregation through colonization seems in the present state of our knowledge to be the ideal and perfectly satisfactory method."

How conclusive was the repeatedly emphasized "conclusive evidence" of feeblemindedness of individuals not personally known to the field worker? A reader with some degree of skepticism has a right to be rather puzzled by the assertion (p. 15): "After some experience, the field worker becomes expert in inferring the condition of those persons who are not seen, from the similarity of the language used in describing them to that

---

it into a bad branch on one hand and a good branch on the other. Each of these branches is traced through the line of the eldest son down to a person of the present generation. On the bad side it ends with Deborah Kallikak, an inmate of the Training School at Vineland; on the good side with the son of a prominent and wealthy citizen of the same family name, now a resident of another State.")

used in describing persons whom she has seen." And while it is stated in the Preface that "the data here presented are, we believe, accurate to a high degree," the very next sentence reads as follows: "It is true that we have made rather dogmatic statements and have drawn conclusions that do not seem scientifically warranted from the data."

The Kallikaks were joined in 1912 by the Nams and the Hill Folk. While, according to the authors (Estabrook and Davenport), the Jukes stood out because of a large proportion of criminals, the Ishmaelites because of pauperism, and the Zeros because of vagrancy, the Nams were characterized chiefly by a preponderance of alcoholism and "lack of ambition." They were congregated in an isolated spot in the mountains of Western Massachusetts.

The Hill Folk, studied by Danielson and Davenport, lived in a small town in the same state; an investigation of two family trees aimed "to show how crime, misery and expense may result from the union of two defective individuals."

In 1916, Kostir, a social worker, told of the family of Sam Sixty. The fictitious last name was chosen because of "the mental endowment of the principal representative, since he had a 60 per cent mental equipment, as measured by the Point Scale." Miss Kostir's conclusion was that "feebleminded parents have feebleminded children" and that "physically vigorous but mentally feeble persons are a social menace today; their children threaten to overwhelm the civilization of the future."

Similar laments came from Minnesota in 1919 when Rogers and Merril reported family history studies of inmates of an institution in that state.

With so much "evidence" made available within a few years, the eugenic guardians of the race and its civilization came forth with emotionally charged blasts. We shall be lost unless something drastic is done. Mankind stands at the crossroads, East of Harvard warned in 1923, after Grant had predicted "the passing of the great race" in 1921 and Stoddard had written in 1922: "In former times, the numbers of the feebleminded were kept down by the stern processes of natural selection, but modern society and philanthropy have protected them and have thus favored their rapid multiplication." In 1928, Pitkin invited the public to worrry with him about the "twilight of the American mind." In Germany, von Behr-Pinnow went even farther and, in a popular booklet published in 1929, spoke of the "dusk of mankind" (*Menschheitsdämmerung*).

All this went on between 1910 and 1930. It did not seem to occur to the preachers of gloom that civilization was indeed in grave danger but that the danger did not come from the mental defectives. The Central European jingoists who unleashed World War One did not have low intelligence quotients. In the decade immediately preceding the rise of Mussolini and Hitler, salvation was expected to come to the human species from the extirpation of the mentally retarded. The one man Hitler, who probably would not have come out too badly in terms of the Binet-Simon scale, did more damage than all the mental defectives since the beginning of history. In fact, it was a novel by Paul Rohrbach, a historian turned writer of fiction, who, allegedly borrowing from the eugenicists, spoke the language of the Nazis when in 1929 he advocated the supremacy of "superman" over "subman." He warned: "Majority of the masses becomes majority of submen — the day of subman is menacingly upon us." The Übermensch was given a free hand to eliminate everybody whom he arbitrarily considered as *Untermensch*.

Inevitably, a reaction was bound to occur in a democratic society. Fernald had joined the chorus of the alarmists in 1912 when he called the feebleminded "a parasitic, predatory class, never capable of self-support or of managing their own affairs," people who "cause unutterable sorrow at home and are a menace and danger to the community." In 1924, he referred to such generalizations as "the legend of the feebleminded" which had prevailed "for nearly two decades": He wrote: "The black charts of the Kallikaks, the Nam Family and the Hill Folk, etc., were most sinister in their significance as showing that certain types of defect were transmitted in accordance with certain genetic laws, and that a majority of the defectives studied were of the hereditary class . . . The feebleminded person became an object of horror and aversion. He was looked upon as an Ishmaelite, a useless, dangerous person, who should be ostracized, sterilized, and segregated for his natural life at public expense." No, he declared, the danger does not come from the defectives as such but rather from the "neglected, untrained, and uncared for defectives."

The eugenicists gave much thought to means of reducing the number of the mentally retarded. A committee of the American Breeders' Association, convening in 1911, reviewed ten possible reactions to the existing problem, with the view of "purging from the blood of the race the innately defective strains." This list, reproduced by Davies and by Landman, contained the following items:

1. *Laissez faire.* This reaction was, of course, the perpetuation of an old-age attitude which had existed in the pre-eugenic past. It had its strongest supporters in certain theological quarters.

2. *Euthanasia.* Even the most frightened people shied away from an off-with-their-heads program.

3. *Restrictive marriage laws and customs.*

4. *Eugenic education.* This was not an altogether new idea. Disselhoff mentioned an 18th-century edict by the Archbishop of Würzburg which admonished the inhabitants of Gerolzhofen to marry persons from other towns in order to put an end to endemic cretinism in their community.

5. *Systems of matings purporting to remove defective traits.*

6. *Scientific breeding.*

7. *Birth control* (Neo-Malthusianism).

8. *General environmental improvement.*

9. *Institutionalization or colonization.*

10. *Sterilization.*

It is worthy of note that the list made no reference to medical or any other kind of research. The overriding thought was: We have decided that the mental have-nots in our midst will, because they are maintained by private and official philanthropy, thrive and multiply and render helpless the dwindling remainder of the intellectual haves. We must get them out of circulation and curtail their propagation.

Hence, of the ten points on the list segregation and sterilization seemed to the committee to promise the best and earliest results. Segregation for life or at least during the reproductive years "must, in the opinion of the committee, be the principal agent used by society in cutting off its supply of defectives." Sterilization was "advocated only as supporting the more important feature of segregation when the latter agency fails to function eugenically."

The sterilization idea was not altogether unprecedented. As far back as in 1897, a bill to this effect was introduced in the Michigan legislature but failed of passage.

In the early 1900's, Dr. H. C. Sharp undertook, without official sanction, to perform "vasectomy" at the Indiana State Reformatory. On March 9, 1907, the state legislature made this legal by enacting the first eugenic sterilization law providing for the prevention of procreation of "confirmed criminals, idiots, imbeciles, and rapists." The constitutionality of this law was challenged, and it was declared invalid by the Supreme Court of Indiana on May 11, 1921. Finally, on March 11, 1927, a new law was enacted and has remained in effect since then.

The State of Washington followed on March 22, 1909; sterilization was allowed as a punitive measure for carnal abuse of young girls, rape, or criminal recidivism. An amended statute in 1921 included feebleminded, insane, and epileptics as well.

California and Connecticut followed in 1909; Nevada, Iowa, and New Jersey in 1911 (the Iowa law was repealed in 1913 to make place for another statute giving the state greater authority; the New Jersey law was declared unconstitutional in 1913). New York enacted a law in 1912 (declared unconstitutional in 1918), Kansas and North Dakota in 1913.

By 1926, sterilization laws had been enacted in twenty-three states. "Properly drawn" laws were declared constitutional by the highest state courts in Idaho, Kansas, Michigan, Nebraska, Oklahoma, Utah, and Virginia, and on May 2, 1927, by the Supreme Court of the United States.

In Canada, Alberta passed a eugenic sterilization law in 1928.

The European countries, according to Lenz, were much slower

about similar legislation. In those with a Catholic plurality the whole idea ran counter to the general theologic orientation. The first sterilization law was enacted in Denmark in July, 1929, providing for the voluntary sterilization of rapists and mental defectives about to be parolled from prisons or institutions. In the same year, similar statutes were introduced in Switzerland (Canton of Vaud) and in Finland.

The less said about the arbitrary orgies of sterilization, castration, and outright massacre in Nazi Germany the better.

It is regrettable, but in keeping with the spirit of the time, that in all sterilization statutes the mentally retarded were lumped together with psychotics, psychopaths, and criminals.

References

Behr-Pinnow, C. von: *Menschheitsdämmerung?* Berlin. 1929.

Danielson, F. A., and Davenport, C. B.: The Hill Folk. Report on a Rural Community of Hereditary Defectives. Eugenic Record Office Memoir No. 1., Cold Spring Harbor, R. I. August 1912.

Davenport, C. B.: *Heredity in Relation to Eugenics.* New York, Henry Holt and Co. 1911, pp. 66-67.

Davies, S. P.: *The Mentally Retarded in Society.* New York, Columbia Univ. Press. 1959, p. 50.

Disselhoff, J.: *Die gegenwärtige Lage der Cretinen, Blödsinnigen und Idioten in den christlichen Ländern.* Bonn, Marcus. 1857, p. 14.

Dugdale, R. L.: *The Jukes.* New York, Putnam. 1877.

East, E. M.: *Mankind at the Crossroads.* New York, Scribner. 1923.

Estabrook, A. H.: *The Jukes in 1915.* Washington, Carnegie Institute. 1916.

——————, and Davenport, C. B.: The Nam Family. A Study in Cacogenics. Eugenics Record Office Memoir No. 2., Cold Spring Harbor, R. I. 1912.

——————, and McDougle, I. E.: *Mongrel Virginians. The Win Tribe.* Baltimore, Williams and Wilkins. 1926.

Fernald, W. E.: Thirty Years Progress in the Care of the Feebleminded. Proc. Asso. Med. Officers of Amer. Instit. for Idiotic and Feebleminded Persons, 1924, 29, 206-219.

Galton, F.: *Inquiries into Human Faculty and Its Development.* London, J. M. Dent & Sons. 1907. (Originally published in 1883.)

Goddard, H. H.: Heredity in Feeblemindedness. *Amer. Breeders Magazine, 1*:165-178, 1910.

——————: *The Kallikak Family;* A Study in the Heredity of Feeblemindedness. New York, MacMillan. 1912.

Grant, M.: *Passing of the Great Race.* New York, Scribner. 1921.

Jörger, J.: Die Familie Zero. *Arch. f. Rassen-u. Gesellschaftsbiologie, 2*:494-559, 1905.

——————: Die Familie Markus. *Ztschr. f. d. ges. Neurol. u. Psychiatrie, 43*:76-116, 1918.

Kostir, M. S.: The Family of Sam Sixty. Ohio Board of Administration Press Publication No. 8, Ohio State Reformatory. January, 1916. (29 pages).

Landman, J. H.: *Human Sterilization. The History of the Movement.* New York, MacMillan. 1932.

Laughlin, H. H.: *Eugenical Sterilization,* New Haven, Amer. Eugenics Society. 1926.

Lenz, F.: *Menschliche Auslese und Rassenhygiene.* Munich, J. F. Lehmann. 1931, p. 267-292.

McCulloch, O. C.: A Study in Social Degradation. Proc. Nat. Conf. Charities and Correction, 15th Annual Session. Ed. by I. C. Barrows. Boston, Geo. H. Ellis. 1888, pp. 154-170.

Pitkin, W. B.: *Twilight of the American Mind.* New York, Simon & Schuster. 1928.

Rogers, A. C., and Merril, A.: *Dwellers in the Vale of Siddem.* Boston, R. G. Badger. 1919.

Rohrbach, P.: *Der Tag des Untermenschen.* Berlin, Safari Verlag. 1929.

Stoddard, T. L.: *Revolt Against Civilization.* New York, Scribner. 1922.

Wiggam, A. E.: *New Decalogue of Science.* Indianapolis, Bobbs Merrill Co. 1923.

——————: *Fruit of the Family Tree.* Ibid. 1924.

Chapter 10

The Dawn of a New Era

According to the *Columbia Encyclopedia,* history, "in its broadest sense, means the past of man and the story of man's institutions." There is no definition of history which tells, or can possibly tell, when the past ceases and the present begins. It is left to the historiographer to decide at which point he feels that his narrative has reached the threshhold of contemporary events.

The story of the care and study of the mentally retarded barely started about a century and a half ago. Much has happened since then.

A few enthusiastic young men, falling in line with the humanitarian concerns for the oppressed and neglected, decided that something must and could be done for the education and treatments of "idiots."

Guggenbühl's short-lived adventure of the Abendberg inaugurated an era of institutional expansion which began in the 1840's and in the following decades encompassed the entire civilized world.

The notion that residential care and training would bring about a complete state of "normalcy" had to be given up; the institutions became more or less permanent places of segregation. Though most of them were headed by medical men, the superintendents found themselves pushed into the roles of general administrators of "institutions," "asylums," "schools," "training schools," or "colonies," but not "hospitals." This does not mean that attention was not given to bodily ailments. It does mean that the physicians in the institutions were almost as isolated from their medical confrères on the outside as the inmates were from the extramural world. The whole issue of mental deficiency was kept out of the academic halls of medical learning; in clinical work, research, and teaching it was treated as if it were non-existent. The few psychiatrists with university connections who devoted themselves to the study of mental deficiency were notable exceptions.

Mental retardation, by whatever name it went, was originally looked upon as a unitary condition. Cretinism, when not used as a synonym for idiocy, was the only known specific subdivision. Down's description of mongolism as a separate form ushered in a series of discoveries of specific conditions associated with mental deficiency. Attempts at etiological classification were introduced. The notion of homogeneity became less convincing.

Those not too conspicuously retarded began to receive educational aid in a few special classes of public schools in Germany, then in Norway, and eventually in several other countries. The question of eligibility for such instruction gave rise to the hope that an answer might be obtained from the psychologists. It came from Binet and Simon as a culmination of efforts inspired by Rousseau and Locke, the diaries kept about the development of individual infants, and the results of questionnaires sent out to gather data about representative numbers of children. A scale for the quantitative assessment of the degree of learning ability ("intelligence") was established. The attainments of developmental psychology laid the groundwork for the beginning and growth of educational psychology.

In brief, the care and study of the mentally retarded had its origin as a *philanthropic* enterprise intended to "cure" severely defective persons in residential settings. This was shared by a few physicians, many educators (especially teachers of deaf-mutes), and dedicated clergymen. The introduction of special classes put the major task into the hands of *educators*. Eventually *psychologists* entered the field in search of reliable criteria for the evaluation of intellectual endowment. Thus philanthropy, education, and psychology were the consecutive godfathers of progress.

This was the state of affairs by 1910. All efforts were bent on doing something for the betterment of the lot and functioning of mentally retarded individuals.

Then came the great "eugenic alarm" which, sparked by Goddard's story of the Kallikaks, pictured the "feebleminded" as a menace to society and to the future of the race, as a cesspool from which rose an unending swarm of criminals, drunkards, paupers, and breeders of ever more defectives. This alarm lasted for about a quarter of a century.

Fortunately, the scare did not halt the constructive efforts which were the heritage of the nineteenth century. Nevertheless, the years between 1910 and about 1935 may be designated as "the great lull." While more institutions were built, while more special classes were added, while the *Heilpädagogik* (remedial pedagogy) movement in Central Europe tried earnestly to improve the educational facilities, while the Binet-Simon and similar tests were applied to tens of thousands of children, all this was basically an implementation of methods begun in the past. Little that was essentially new was brought to light.

A new era dawned in 1934 when Fölling in Norway discovered phenylpyruvic acid oligophrenia (phenylketonuria) as a metabolic disturbance which could eventually become reversible by means of proper dietary regulation. This contribution, termed "one of the great discoveries in medical history" by Clemens E. Benda, at long last made the issue of mental deficiency appear respectable as a legitimate field of research in the biological sciences. Slowly and at first reluctantly, the medical profession began to take an interest.

During "the great lull," the mental hygiene movement, brought into being by Clifford Beers in 1909 as a national concern, resulted in 1922 in the establishment of child guidance clinics, presided by psychiatrists with the collaboration of psychologists and social workers. There was half-hearted regard of the problems of retardation in terms of testing and disposition (recommendation of institutional placement, special class, vocational adjustment). But neither these clinics nor psychiatric or pediatric teaching centers saw retardation as worthy of full inclusion in their scientific concerns. This was left almost entirely to the "specialists," mostly connected with institutions in more or less splendid isolation.

In 1930, a children's psychiatric clinic was established at the Harriet Lane Home, the Department of Pediatrics of the Johns Hopkins Hospital. With the exception of a short-lived similar attempt in Vienna, it was the first working alliance between psychiatry and pediatrics. This unit made it a point to integrate clinical and investigative occupation with retarded children and their families with the rest of its work. Its director had this to say in a guest editorial of the *American Journal of Mental Deficiency* 46: 225-226, 1941:

"The students of mental deficiency, absorbed with their own specialized topic, failed to see how they could be benefited by something that seemed to be out of their range. Some child guidance clinics, with a haughty let-George-do-it attitude, refused to be bothered with feebleminded children, whom they mistakenly regarded as uninteresting material. The behaviorists wished feeblemindedness out of existence by the simple expedient of ignoring it completely. A small contingent of psychoanalysts speculated it out of existence by ascribing it to 'emotional blocking.'

"But eventual approximation was inevitable.

"The luxury, or at least seeming luxury, of dispensing child guidance to intelligent children only had to give way to the real needs of the communities, which expected assistance with all of their problems and not just an arbitrarily selected portion. This virtue, though sometimes embraced reluctantly, had its own reward in better acquaintance with the desiderata and attainments of special education and the realization that 'the feebleminded' are as heterogeneous a group of human beings as any other, deserving of the scientist's investigation and the physician's sympathy. Intellectual limitations are inextricably linked with the nation-wide problem of juvenile delinquency, the much-discussed question of the course of the epilepsies, the symptoms and sequels of cerebral and endocrine disorders, the still puzzling riddle of heredity, and other issues involving major preplexities of clinics, courts, schools, and society in general. The behavior problems of the intelligent, less intelligent, and unintelligent cannot possibly be assigned to separate categories. Occupation with mental deficiency is a legitimate part of child (and adult) psychiatry — not merely an appendix but one of its integral functions."

While such sentiments were voiced with increasing frequency, an important impetus came from a group which, first organized in 1950, grew to become a major stimulant. The NARC (National Association for Retarded Children), begun by a small handful of people, had in 1959 an individual membership of about 50,000 "parents and friends of mentally retarded children." Under the leadership of Dr. Grover Powers, an eminent pediatrician, its Scientific Research Advisory Board called together leading representatives of every specialty which possibly could have a hand in the study, prevention, and care of mental retardation: genetics, pathology, obstetrics, pediatrics, neurology, child psychiatry, psychology, biochemistry, education, sociology, etc.

The "eugenic alarm" began to be dispersed by the recognition of the diversity of conditions leading to, or accompanied by, mental retardation, with or without varying types of hereditary involvement. This made previous statistics and speculations, based on the assumed amorphousness of feeblemindedness, scientifically invalid. New discoveries in the field of genetics established a more solid foundation than had existed before.

A future historian, taking up where this book leaves off, may find the major areas of progress epitomized in a memorable event which took place on December 6, 1962. The Joseph P. Kennedy, Jr. Foundation, founded in 1946 to foster programs of care, training, and treatment of the retarded and to promote research, presented the first awards for outstanding work in the field. The recipients were:

1. *The National Association for Retarded Children* "for its outstanding role in awakening the nation to the problems of mental retardation and for proving, through a diversity of means, that the retarded can be helped."

2. *Dr. Samuel A. Kirk*, director of the Institute for Research on Exceptional Children at the University of Illinois for his untiring efforts pertaining to the early education of retarded children.

3. *Dr. Ivar Asbjörn Fölling*, retired chief of the University Hospital Clinical Laboratory at Oslo, Norway "for bringing on the new awareness of inborn errors of metabolism through his discovery of phenylketonuria."

4. *Dr. Murray L. Barr*, head of the Department of Microscopic Anatomy of the University of Ontario, for his discovery of sex chromatin.

5. *Dr. Joe Hin Tijo*, a Dutch-Indonesian, visiting scientist of the National Institute of Health in Bethesda, Maryland, for his discovery of the exact number of chromosomes in man.

6. *Dr. Jerome Lejeune*, director of the Department of Genetics at the University of Paris, for his discovery of chromosomal abnormalities associated with mongolism.

Mental retardation has become a respectable topic of scientific research. Through the NARC, public interest and stimulation are assured. The international aspect of the awards points to the universality of the problem and the collaboration of scientists the world over.

On February 5, 1963, John F. Kennedy, the President of the United States, sent a message to the Congress "relative to mental illness and mental retardation," on the basis of a report from a specially appointed panel of experts, suggesting "a national program to combat mental retardation."

A new era has begun. It is reminiscent of the enthusiasm of Itard, Seguin, Guggenbühl, and Howe. The difference is that medicine, sociology, education, and psychology have furnished tools more precise than existed then. But it must be pointed out that we would not be where we are now if it had not been for the early pioneers in many lands.

Goethe has said that the history of a science is the science itself. As the search for further knowledge of the causes, prevention and treatment of mental retardation goes on, history continues being made.

Index